The Hunt for the
WHOOPING CRANES

The Hunt for the

WHOOPING

They tempt the sun to sport amid their plumes,
They tempt the water, or the gleaming ice,
To show them a fair image; 'tis themselves,
Their own fair forms upon the glimmering plain,
Painted more soft and fair as they descend
Almost to touch;—then up again aloft,
Up with a sally and a flash of speed,
As if they scorned both resting place and rest!

from *Water Fowl*
by William Wordsworth

CRANES

a Natural History Detective Story

by J.J. McCOY

Maps and drawings by Rey Abruzzi

PAUL S. ERIKSSON, *PUBLISHER*
FOREST DALE, VERMONT

10 9 8 7 6 5 4 3 2 1

First paperback edition

Library of Congress Cataloging-in-Publication Data

McCoy, J. J. (Joseph J.), 1917-
 The hunt for the whooping cranes: a natural his-
tory detective story / by J.J.McCoy; maps and draw-
ings by Rey Abruzzi. — 1st pkb. ed.
 p. cm.
 Originally published: New York: Lothrop, Lee &
Shepard Co., 1966. Includes bibliographical refer-
ences (p.) and index.
 ISBN 0-8397-3500-6 (pbk.)
 1. Whooping crane. 2. Birds, protection of —
North America.
 I. Title.
QL 696.G84M375   1966   96-22081
639.9'7831 — dc20   CIP

Photograph on page 16 by F. W. Lahrman,
from the National Audubon Society

To the late
Robert Porter Allen,
fellow Pennsylvanian,
who played a major role
in the search for the
summer nesting grounds
of the whooping cranes.

Preface

by Carl W. Buchheister
President, National Audubon Society

In April of 1933, the last heath hen in the world died on
Martha's Vineyard, an island just off the coast of Cape
Cod in Massachusetts.

The bird could not have known that his death was the
death of his kind, but men knew, and the people of
Martha's Vineyard paused to consider what had happened
in their midst. A creature that had been enormously abundant only a few hundred years before had been destroyed
beyond the power of nature to restore: its numbers reduced in an incredibly short space of time until there
were too few to survive. Millions of years of evolution and
the interaction of powerful forces beyond our under-
standing had gone into the heath hen's making. Mankind
could not create, or even re-create, this form of life. Men
could only destroy.

Henry Beetle Hough, editor of the local newspaper, wrote:

> There is no survivor, there is no future, there is no life to be created in this form again. We are looking upon the uttermost finality which can be written, glimpsing the darkness which will not know another ray of light. We are in touch with the reality of extinction.

The extinction of the heath hen is only a small part of the havoc that man has wrought on himself and his environment. Looking back on his comparatively short history, we see that he has turned green forests into barren, flood-ridden gashes on the face of the earth. The water of sweet rushing streams and rivers gives life no longer, but is gray, sluggish matter, carrying garbage, detergent, poison, death to wildlife, and no refreshment to man. The presence of DDT in Arctic penguins indicates that we may have poisoned the entire length and breadth of the earth. The miraculous spark that is animal life, burning as brightly in the most insignificant creature as in man, and which current space exploration leads us to think is sustained within our solar system by earth alone, has been extinguished for many species.

It is a gloomy picture. The future might look hopelessly dismal were it not for a glimmer of light: call it the divine spark, man's soul, or the continuing evolution of his intelligence into a greater capability—it is there. Mankind seems to be slowly maturing, to be accepting his responsibility for himself and to the earth that gives him life. This book, *The Hunt for the Whooping Cranes*, recounts one of the more hopeful episodes in this evolution.

The story begins in 1945, when there were fewer than thirty whooping cranes left. At that time the area in Texas where they passed the winter had already been made a national wildlife refuge. There, they were protected. Each spring, however, the small band took to the air and flew northward to their summer breeding grounds, as whooping cranes had done for more than a million years. They passed over Oklahoma, and Kansas, and followed the Platte River through Nebraska. Somewhere, probably in the lake country of Canada, but possibly even in Alaska, the great white birds came to rest and settled down to rear their young. The question was—where? The cranes appeared to be encountering danger in their secret place or along the migratory route, for each year fewer and fewer returned to Texas. Unless the breeding grounds could be found and protected, the future looked dim.

And so the great hunt was on. It was sponsored by three organizations working together: the U.S. Fish and Wildlife Service, the Canadian Wildlife Service, and the National Audubon Society. It was given the moral support of thousands, perhaps millions, of Americans and Canadians. There were those who participated in publicity campaigns; those who watched the skies, hoping for some glimpse of the elusive birds and some indication of their route; and the sportsmen in the field, who cautioned each other not to shoot any large white bird.

From many parts of the world we received encouragement; it was sorely needed, for at times we became des-

pairing and desperate. When the cranes crossed the
Canadian border, it was as if they were swallowed up by
the vast wilderness.

Eventually, almost a million square miles were
searched; then success came from an unexpected source.
. . . But no, that is Mr. McCoy's story and I leave *him* to
tell it.

Acknowledgments

I am indebted to a number of organizations, agencies and individuals who contributed suggestions and information for the first edition of *The Hunt For The Whooping Cranes*. I am especially indebted to the National Audubon Society for placing its whooping crane-research reports at my disposal. Without these basic works, this book could not have been written.

The United States Fish and Wildlife Service and the Canadian Wildlife Service were most helpful when I started this story of the search for the nesting grounds of the rare whooping cranes. These agencies, along with the International Crane Foundation, and Calgary Zoo, have also provided data for the epilogue, "How The Whoopers Fare Today."

I wish to thank the following individuals for their contributions to the writing of my narrative of the eleven-year search for the breeding grounds of the whooping cranes:
John H. Baker, President Emeritus, The National Audubon Society; Dr. Fred Bard, Dr. William A. Fuller, Robert H. Smith, Dr. Olin S. Pettingill, Jr., Dr. Lawrence H. Walkinshaw, Roland Clement, Robert Allen, and Robert G. Hudson.

I am also grateful to the publishers of *The Christian Science Monitor* for permission to reproduce their editorial, "On Cranes and People," from a September, 1954 issue of that newspaper. I am also indebted to John Vosburgh, then editor of *Audubon Magazine*, for allowing me to quote Bob Allen's letter from Aklavik, which appeared in the September/October, 1948 issue of the magazine.

My thanks to Brian Johns, Canadian Wildlife Service; Rob Nelson, International Crane Foundation; Beverly Fletcher, U.S. Fish and Wildlife Service; Ian Gray, director of the Calgary Zoo; and Mike Fisher, U.S. Fish and Wildlife Service for providing information on the present status of the whooping cranes.

—J.J. McC.

Contents

Maps

The Hunt for the
WHOOPING CRANES

WHOOPING CRANE

[Grus americana]

A large white crane native to North
America. Larger than a Sandhill
Crane or Great Blue Heron. Very
tall—over five feet in height. Wingspread—about seven feet. Adult plumage is white with black-tipped wings.
Top of head is devoid of feathers and
shows a red patch. Young cranes are
cinnamon-colored. Found only in
North America. A very rare bird on
the verge of extinction.

ONE

Off to the Northwest

Aransas National Wildlife Refuge, Texas, mid-April, 1945: The sun warmed the brackish water in the salt flats that fringed the Blackjack Peninsula on the southern coast of Texas. On the tide-sculptured shore, two biologists were crouching in a canvas blind. A powerful telescope poked through a hole in the blind. One of the men slowly swung the telescope in a wide arc, carefully examining the vast expanse of marsh and tidal flats. The telescope stopped moving and the observer quickly nudged the other biologist.

"There's a whooper!" he exclaimed.

The two men took turns watching the whooping crane through the telescope. Even though the crane was nearly a quarter of a mile away, the telescope brought the bird into sharp focus. The big white crane waded gingerly in

A whooping crane   *by Allan D. Cruickshank, from National Audubon Society*

the shallow water. He was almost as tall as a man, standing over five feet high on black, stiltlike legs.

The whooper halted his wading and stood motionless, scarlet-capped head poised a foot above the water. His bright eyes stared at a blue crab sidling along the bottom of the salt flat. The crane leaned forward ever so slowly, and remained absolutely still in that position. Then, extending his wings for balance, he lunged, stabbing his strong bill into the water and neatly spearing the crab. He shook it fiercely, and the force sent legs and claws flying in all directions. A tremendous gulp thrust the crab down the bird's long gullet.

Inside the blind, a biologist maneuvered the telescope as the crane strode out of the water and up onto higher ground. Now that his hunger was appeased, the crane relaxed in the warm sun. He lowered his head, brought up a foot and scratched away a piece of crab which was clinging to his beak. With this after-dinner chore out of the way, the crane preened himself, digging his beak into glossy white feathers.

Suddenly the shadow of a cloud drifted over him. He cocked his head sideways, peering up at the cumulus clouds skittering northward across the sky. A shudder passed over his body and then was gone. Like the other whooping cranes in the sloughs of the Blackjack Peninsula, he had been restless for several weeks. Now he felt a powerful urge drawing him up to the sky. It was time to migrate. The gonadal cycle, which some ornithologists believe governs the migrations of birds, was at work in the big whooper.

A strong gulf breeze whistled in over the sloughs and

Three whoopers on the Texas Gulf Coast circa 1945.
—*Photo by National Audubon Society*

salt flats and the whooper braced himself against the
gusts. He glanced to his right, where three other whoopers had emerged from a clump of tall sedges and were
meandering through the water, hunting crabs. The big
whooper's body tensed. From deep inside his tightly
coiled windpipe, a cry spun upward and boomed out over
the flats.

Ker-loo! Ker-lee-oo!

The loud call startled the nearby cranes. They looked
up from their feeding, water dribbling from their bills.
Again the lone crane hurled his war whoop over the
sloughs and flats.

Ker-loo! Ker-lee-oo!

His whole body quivering with excitement, the big
crane dropped into a crouch. The great head and long
neck were stretched forward and parallel to the ground.
Holding his wings aloft, the crane ran swiftly, gaining
speed with each giant stride. A mighty flick of his wings, a
bounding leap, and he was airborne. Rapid wingbeats
scooped air under the gleaming white body, lifting him in
a long, sloping flight up over the sloughs and flats. Up, up,
and up he climbed, as though he meant to overtake the
wind-buffeted clouds and ride them north. But when he
was several hundred feet above the flats, he leveled off
and swung into a leisurely circle over the other cranes.
From his command post in the sky, he hurled repeated
whoops down to the earthbound birds.

The other cranes responded to his challenging calls.
Hastening out of the water, they picked their way onto
the sandy shore of a small island. One by one they raced
over the ground, rising up with flailing wings. Mighty

wingbeats brought them up to the first crane's altitude and then all four birds chased each other in a great merry-go-round high above the Aransas Wildlife Refuge. Long legs trailed out behind the cranes like tailskids on an airplane, and their satin-white feathers glistened in the sun. Again and again the birds blared out their bugle calls, announcing to the handful of whooping cranes still down in the sloughs and flats that it was time to leave their wintering grounds.

Breaking out of their follow-the-leader formation, the four cranes formed sides and crossed back and forth over the sky in graceful flight, dodging each other with batlike agility. They soon abandoned this game and launched into a thrilling aerial ballet. Led by the big whooper, the cranes looped, rolled, and sideslipped with a recklessness born of their need to migrate. Suddenly, as if from a signal from their leader, the cranes plummeted toward a sandy island off the Blackjack Peninsula. They pulled out of their dive a few feet above the island and—in perfect unison—streaked back up into the sky.

Drawn by some irresistible force, the lead crane broke away from the others and flew northward. He flew solo for perhaps a quarter of a mile, then veered around and raced back to his companions. He darted in and out among them, urging them to follow. Now the other cranes were ready to go, too. They formed a lopsided V formation behind the leader, great heads pointing toward the northwest. With the big crane leading the way, the cranes hurried after the fleeting clouds and soon became glittering dots in the sky.

*   *   *

Whooping cranes   *by Albert Simmons, from National Audubon Society*

Within a few days, the remainder of the small band of
wild whooping cranes rose up from the Aransas sloughs
and flats on their annual migration to their nesting
grounds. On this particular occasion, twenty-seven birds
—all that remained of the wild whooping cranes—set out
on the long and hazardous trip north. And as the last faint
Ker-loo! spiraled down to the sloughs, the biologists hidden in the canvas blind gazed thoughtfully after the dis-

appearing cranes. They wondered, as others did, where the whoopers nested.

Nobody knew the destination of the cranes after the great birds left Aransas. All that was known was that they traveled in a northwesterly direction, passing over Texas, Oklahoma, Kansas, Nebraska, South Dakota, North Dakota, and on into Saskatchewan, Canada. Spotters reported the cranes when the birds passed over into Saskatchewan, but after that hardly anything was ever seen or heard of them; they simply vanished into the vast Canadian wilderness. If a whooper was sighted later on, the chances were that it was a "summer wanderer" and not one of the breeding birds.

Each fall the whooping cranes flew back to the Aransas Refuge with several youngsters. But twentieth century man, despite his helicopters and tracking devices, could only wonder and speculate as to where the cranes nested. Occasional searches by amateur and professional naturalists had all proved fruitless.

There were those who sneered at the concern over where the whoopers nested. What difference did it make? After all, the big birds returned to Aransas on the Texas coast every fall and stayed until spring. Biologists, conservationists, and naturalists could observe the cranes on the wintering grounds.

There was an ominous note to this line of thinking, however. Nobody knew for how long a time the handful of whooping cranes would continue to return to Aransas. The whooping crane, *Grus americana,* was a species already in a steep dive toward extinction. The small flock that wintered in Aransas contained the only wild whooping cranes left in the entire world.

Never a plentiful species since the Pleistocene epoch, the great birds had steadily lost ground in their fight for survival. Unless some drastic step was taken—and taken soon—the whoopers would completely disappear as a species. They would join the ranks of the heath hen, great auk, passenger pigeon, and Eskimo curlew—extinct species which were now to be seen only in museum collections and bird books.

TWO

Dossier on the Whooping Cranes

Surprisingly enough, those interested in the plight of the whooping cranes found a large dossier on the birds—an accumulation of reports, notes, and observations going back to colonial times. Unfortunately, much of the information was unconfirmed and unreliable, often sheer guesswork on the part of the reporter or observer. But it was a basis from which to do further studies.

The whooping and other cranes belong to the order *Gruiformes,* which contains all of the cranelike birds, including coots, rails, sun grebes, gallinules, and sun bitterns. The suborder is composed of the limpkins and the family *Gruidae,* or cranes. There are four genera in the *Gruidae,* but only two of them are found in North America: *Grus americana* (whooping crane) and *G. canadensis* (sandhill crane) and its subspecies. Nineteenth century

28

archeological investigations revealed that the whooping crane existed in Florida as far back as the Pleistocene epoch.

Altogether, there are fourteen full species and twenty-three races of cranes distributed throughout the world, and they are found on every continent except South America. But the whooping crane is the only species faced with immediate extinction.

Early reports on the whooping cranes were vague, incomplete, and sometimes downright confusing. English and French explorers roaming the wilderness along the eastern coast and inland waterways of North America told of seeing "large white cranes."

Captain Philip Amadas, the English explorer, landed on Wokokon Island in Pamlico Sound off the North Carolina coast in 1585. Pamlico Sound, separated from the Atlantic Ocean by a string of barrier beaches, appeared to be a haven for all kinds of waterfowl and wading birds. Captain Amadas, according to the British historian, Richard Hakluyt, came upon a large number of birds on Wokokon Island. Amadas and his party fired their arquebuses (clumsy, primitive firearms) and watched the air fill with flocks of birds, including "great white cranes."

Later, in 1615, Samuel de Champlain explored Lake Ontario. This intrepid explorer, map maker, fur trader, colonizer, and author covered considerable territory in his travels over northeastern North America. On the Lake Ontario expedition, Champlain and his men sighted many birds, some of which were large and cranelike. Champlain recorded them as "cranes which were as white as swans."

But the birds seen by Amadas and Champlain, even though described as "white cranes," were never confirmed as whooping cranes. No specimens were taken and no description, other than that of the white color, was given by either Amadas or Champlain. The "cranes" seen by both explorers might have been egrets or herons, even though later observations revealed that whoopers did live in the North Carolina and Lake Ontario regions.

The first reliable report of the whooping crane was set down by Mark Catesby, the English naturalist, in 1722. Catesby, intrigued by the variety and abundance of plants and animals in the New World, devoted seven years to the study of the natural history of South Carolina, Georgia, and Florida. He roamed all over these three states, collecting and classifying plants and animals. On one of his trips he obtained the whole pelt of a white crane from an Indian. An astute observer, Catesby sensed that he had a new species in hand and carefully made drawings of the head and neck. He also wrote a full description of the whooper pelt, which eventually was included, along with the drawings, in Catesby's book, *Natural History of Carolina, Florida and the Bahama Islands.*

The Indian who gave Catesby the whooper pelt told the naturalist that in winter the big cranes could be found along the rivers near the "Big Sea" (Atlantic Ocean); in summer, they flew off to the mountains. Other than this meager information, Catesby's record on the whooping crane was mainly anatomical. There is no mention of any further encounters with whooping cranes. Apparently, he never saw another one, dead or alive.

Catesby's report and description of the whooping crane

specimen was duly examined by other naturalists. Carolus
Linnaeus, the father of modern taxonomy, bestowed the
scientific name *Grus americana alba* on the new species.
Later, when it was clear that there were no subspecies,
the name was shortened to *Grus americana*.

In the latter part of the eighteenth century, William
Bartram, the Quaker naturalist from Philadelphia, spent
five years traveling through the South and parts of the
Midwest. He was the son of the famous Philadelphia
botanist, John Bartram, who founded the first botanical
garden in America. Like his father, William had no for-
mal education, but traveled widely and learned his natural history in the field. He was known for his careful
descriptions of plants and a list of American birds.

During a trip to Florida, William and his father saw
large flocks of wading birds, some of which William called
"storks," and others "whooping cranes." Actually, William didn't see any storks; he misapplied names, calling
whooping cranes "storks" and designating sandhill
cranes as "whooping cranes." It was a confusing record,
but the Bartrams really did see whoopers.

William later made a trip to the Mississippi River Delta
where he reported sightings of whooping cranes (he still
called them "storks") feeding among flocks of what probably were sandhill cranes and snow geese. Extending his
travels, William went up the Mississippi to Natchez, and
made daily entries in a journal along the way. Included in
the journal were repeated references to "storks," which, of
course, were whooping cranes.

John James Audubon, tramping the fields, marshes,
and woods in search of bird subjects to paint for his great

work, *Birds of America,* saw a whooping crane near
Louisville, Kentucky, in the early spring of 1810. His
companion on the trip was the dour Scots naturalist, Alexander Wilson. Audubon later did a magnificent painting
of another whooper in Louisiana.

While Audubon, the colorful naturalist and bird
painter, needs little introduction, the brooding Alexander
Wilson is not so well known, although he contributed
much to our knowledge of early American ornithology.
The son of a Scots weaver, Wilson emigrated to America
from Scotland, after serving a short prison term for writing libelous verse, and landed at Newcastle, Delaware, in
1794. Dividing his time between teaching and nature
study, he started to make a collection of paintings of all
birds found in America.

Like Audubon, Wilson roamed the wilderness searching for new birds to paint. He reported sighting whooping cranes on the Waccamaw River in South Carolina and
in the salt marshes near Cape May, New Jersey. Wilson
had a sharp eye and wrote that whooping cranes fed on
marine worms in the Cape May tidal marshes; only re-
cently, biologists have verified the fact that these worms
are a staple in the crane's diet.

Wilson's observations and reports on the whooping
crane helped bring the early eastern range of the birds
into better perspective, although his reports were by no
means complete—in fact, some of them were sheer guesswork. For instance, he stated that the whoopers flew to
South America; he actually didn't know that they flew
there, but he assumed that they did. This surmise later
proved to be unfounded, since no whooping cranes, or any

Painting of whooping crane by John J. Audubon,
from National Audubon Society

cranes, were ever reported in South America.

Despite the inaccuracies and guesswork, Wilson's data on the whooping cranes in eastern America were significant contributions to the scant information available to ornithologists. But just how many whoopers were on the East coast in the early part of the nineteenth century, and where they were located, are questions that were never answered.

In the West, Meriwether Lewis and William Clark, guided by the Shoshone Indian woman, Sacagawea, explored the Louisiana Purchase for Thomas Jefferson. The Lewis and Clark expedition sighted whoopers on the upper Missouri in the spring of 1805 and again on the Columbia River in the fall of the same year. No specimens were taken, though, and as a result the descriptions recorded in the expedition's journal were terse and lacked scientific detail.

The journal entry made on the whooping cranes in the spring of 1805 stated: "Saw some large white cranes pass up the river. These are the largest birds of that genus common to the country through which the Missouri and Mississippi pass. They are perfectly white except the large feathers of the first two joints of the wing, which are black." Again, in the fall of 1805, the journal states: "October 26, 1805. Columbia river near The Dalles (Oregon Territory). Saw a great number of white cranes flying in different directions very high."

Twentieth century ornithologists have viewed this last entry with caution. Were all the cranes seen by the Lewis and Clark expedition whoopers? Or was the flock composed of whooping and sandhill cranes? There is no way of really knowing.

In the north, the first accurate information on whooping cranes in Canada came from Samuel Hearne, explorer for the Hudson's Bay Company. Hearne was not a naturalist, but he possessed excellent powers of observation. He reported seeing an occasional pair of whooping cranes on Hudson Bay in the springs of 1770 and 1771. The whoopers stayed in the open swamps, by the sides of rivers, and along the margins of lakes and ponds, where Hearne observed them eating frogs and small fish. He noted that the whooper parents seldom had more than two offspring, and that all the great cranes flew southward in the fall.

Samuel Hearne was an unusual man. In his twenties at the time of the whooper sightings, Hearne was typical of the career explorers in the Hudson's Bay Company. He displayed a capacity to travel fast and far through the vast wilderness, got along well with the Indians, and kept clear, accurate journals. Endowed with tremendous self-discipline, he was a forerunner of the tough, leathery men who would later build the great Canadian fur empires.

The whooping crane dossier also contained reports on the southwestern range of the big birds. Colonel George A. McCall, U.S. Army, was assigned to posts in Texas and other parts of the Southwest in 1845. While on a long trip from San Antonio, Texas, to the Upper Rio Grande in New Mexico, McCall sighted a lone whooping crane near Arroyo Hondo, north of San Antonio. Later, Colonel McCall observed pairs and groups of three or four whooping cranes on the Texas coast near Corpus Christi.

McCall reported that the whoopers preferred the water's edge of riverbanks or fresh-water ponds, as well as the sandy parts of salt flats. By contrast, he noted that the sandhill cranes—he called them "brown cranes"—stayed on the low prairies away from the bays and rivers. McCall's report that he saw whooping cranes was given considerable credence a hundred years later when biologists, studying both whooping and sandhill cranes, confirmed his observations on the preferred areas of the two birds.

Old reports of whooping cranes in the central part of the United States indicate that the big birds were frequently seen in the plains states during much of the nineteenth century. In the period between 1864 and 1884, the whooper's breeding range was reported to include sites in Iowa, Illinois, Minnesota, North Dakota, Saskatchewan, Manitoba, and the District of Mackenzie (Northwest Territories, Canada). The over-all range of the whoopers at this time reached from the Arctic coast to central Mexico and from Utah to New Jersey and South Carolina. Prior to 1870, it is estimated that the population of wild whooping cranes remained stable at somewhere between 1,300 and 1,400 birds.

Not many nineteenth century biologists and naturalists were familar with the whooping crane, though, mainly because the bird seldom was sighted in the eastern part of the country. However, the noted ornithologist, William Patterson Turnbull, saw whoopers near Beesley's Point, west of Ocean City, New Jersey, in 1857.

After the Civil War, land-hungry settlers streamed westward, pushing the Indians off the prairies and the whooping cranes and other wildlife out of the marshes and sloughs. Sharp plowshares bit into fertile sod and turned the wild prairies into tame farmland. Marshes and wetlands were drained. The whooping cranes retreated from the grasping tentacles of civilization: by 1894, not a single whooping crane nest was found in the original breeding range in the United States. By 1926, the total number of whoopers left on the North American continent hovered between twenty-five and thirty birds.

This strikingly beautiful bird was teetering on the edge of extinction, but not many people were aware of the whooper's plight. In fact, few except professional ornithologists and conservationists had ever heard of the whooping cranes. And even in the ranks of the professionals, interest in the crane's predicament was only lukewarm. The big cranes were fighting a lone battle against overwhelming odds.

Happily a few specialists realized that the number of whooping cranes had dwindled to a dangerously low point, and these men sounded the alarm. In 1923, Dr. William T. Hornaday, a noted zoologist and conservationist, predicted that the whooping crane would be the next North American species to be totally exterminated. At the time, Hornaday was Director of the New York Zoological Park, and he managed to obtain a whooping crane for the park. He hoped to find a mate for the bird, his idea being to breed the two whoopers and start a captive flock. But he searched in vain for another whooper: the big cranes were too scarce and wary of human beings, and kept well out of the way of all would-be trappers. The whoopers were so rare, in fact, that an Englishman once offered $1,000 for a pair. No one ever filled the order.

Some persons believed the whooping crane already extinct in the 1920's. The *Saturday Evening Post* in 1923 carried an article by Hal Evarts that more or less served as an obituary notice for the whoopers. The article stated that another American bird had passed into oblivion; that the whooping crane, perhaps the most majestic of all our birds, was extinct.

Percy A. Taverner, author of *The Birds of Canada* (1926), wrote that the whooping crane had been practically exterminated within the past thirty years. And Arthur C. Bent, in his monumental *Life Histories,* observed that the whooping crane had steadily decreased in numbers and was entirely gone from much of its former range. Actually, when the maze of speculation was pushed aside, nobody knew just how many whoopers were left or where they lived.

A few dedicated ornithologists and conservationists kept their eyes on the whooping crane's fight for survival. One of these men was Professor Myron Swenk, the eminent Nebraska ornithologist. Professor Swenk collected, collated, and interpreted reports and observations on the whoopers, and published a paper, "The Present Status of the Whooping Crane" (1933), in which he presented the number of whoopers observed in Nebraska each spring and autumn over a twenty-year period. The professor optimistically reported at one time that about 100 whooping cranes were left in North America. Later, he realized this figure was way out of line, that his observers had erred as to the number of cranes. Professor Swenk and others soon became aware that nobody really knew how many whoopers remained; all they did know was that the wild flock was so small as to almost escape notice.

But the dirge for the whooping crane was being sung prematurely. The cranes were not extinct yet, nor were they ready to give up the struggle. In the 1930's, bird watchers jubilantly reported a small band of whooping cranes in the coastal marshes of Louisiana. Soon afterward another group of whoopers was observed wintering on the Texas coast. These Texas cranes were sighted on the fabulous King Ranch and also on the St. Charles Ranch on the Blackjack Peninsula which jutted out into San Antonio Bay and Aransas Bay. The Louisiana and Texas sightings were the first reliable records of the wintering grounds of the rare whoopers.

Observers continued to see the birds both in Louisiana and on the Blackjack Peninsula until 1937, when the whoopers wintering on the King Ranch disappeared. In this same year, the U.S. Fish and Wildlife Service, in an effort to preserve wintering grounds for waterfowl on the gulf coast, acquired the St. Charles Ranch on Blackjack Peninsula from Leroy G. Denman, Sr. At the time—and it was really in the "nick of time"—only fourteen whoopers had been reported as spending the winter on the peninsula and nearby Matagorda and St. Joseph Islands.

The U.S. Fish and Wildlife Service converted the peninsula into the Aransas Migratory Waterfowl Refuge— now known as the Aransas National Wildlife Refuge. Dr. Ira N. Gabrielson, Chief of the Service at the time, was a dedicated conservationist who had seen whooping cranes in Kansas when he was a boy, and in 1911 reported the last one to be observed in his home state. The first manager of the Aransas Refuge was James O. Stevenson. Although not created solely for the benefit of the whooping cranes, the establishment of the Refuge meant that for six months of the year, at least, the birds would be protected.

It was the first practical step in moving them back from the precipice of extinction.

The U.S. Fish and Wildlife Service is a branch of the Department of the Interior. Its chief concern is the protection of game fish, birds, and mammals, as well as the maintenance of national refuges. In a progress-minded country such as ours, this is an important responsibility; sometimes it becomes a difficult task.

When Aransas was established, waterfowl wintering on the gulf coast were in danger. True, they were not facing extinction as were the whooping cranes, but their situation was serious enough. Drainage of marshes and thousands of potholes had destroyed valuable waterfowl habitats. Wetlands were also sorely needed by shore birds and fur-bearing mammals. Pollution of marshes and waterways with oil and pesticides was another threat to wildlife. Elsewhere in the country, waterfowl and wading birds were endangered by loss of habitats and overshooting by hunters. Thus, the establishment of the Aransas Refuge was a much needed measure in the protection of our wildlife.

Best known as the wintering grounds of the whooping cranes, the Aransas National Wildlife Refuge is situated about halfway down the Texas coast on the Blackjack Peninsula, approximately seventy-five miles north of Corpus Christi. The privately owned Matagorda and St. Joseph Islands are between the peninsula and the Gulf of Mexico. The Refuge is composed of 47,261 acres of extensive grasslands, blackjack and live oak forests, tidal flats and sloughs, marshy swales, ponds and lakes. It is an ideal

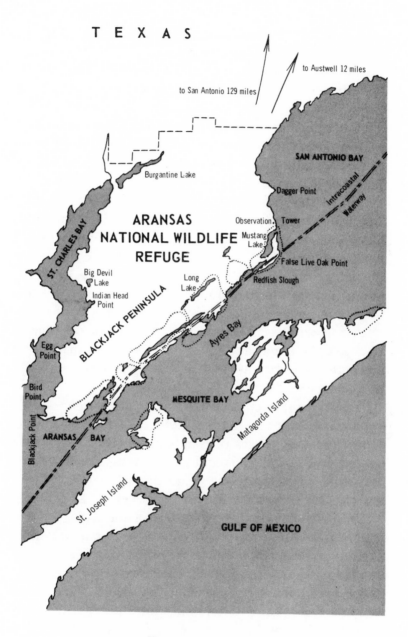

The Aransas Refuge

region for a wildlife refuge. There are fifty-five miles of
shore line which provide important habitats for all kinds
of migratory waterfowl. In the southeastern section of the
peninsula lies a strip of flat land, about fifteen miles long
and from one to three miles wide. This region is the favorite feeding ground of the whooping cranes, and also of
thousands of ducks and geese.

Most of the ducks wintering at Aransas are pintails,
American widgeons, gadwells, buffleheads, and ruddy
ducks. Canada, snow, and blue geese gabble loudly on the
ponds and lakes. Since it possesses an extensive shore line,
the Refuge lures many shore and wading birds. Resident
herons include the common, snowy, reddish, great blue,
little blue, green, and Louisiana; in summer, the rare
roseate spoonbills visit Aransas from their offshore islands.
Almost a thousand sandhill cranes gather in small flocks
along the salt flats, wet swales, and low-growing bush.
And, of course, there are the whooping cranes.

Nearly 300 species of birds have been recorded within
the boundaries of the Aransas Refuge. At migration time,
more than 140 species of songbirds cluster in the trees
around the headquarters and elsewhere on the Blackjack
Peninsula. These songbirds fly northward up the coastline
in the spring en route to their breeding grounds.

Birds of prey soar through and over the Refuge at migration time; some hawks spend the winter in the area.
Kestrels and red-tailed hawks are winter residents in the
wooded sections of the Refuge. Harriers, or marsh hawks,
course over open areas, the sun glinting off their white
rump patches. White-tailed hawks hunt prey in the more
isolated regions of the Refuge. Occasionally, a pair of bald

eagles occupy an area on the peninsula. And Audubon's caracara, the strange hawk with the habits of a vulture, is a permanent resident.

Wildlife on Aransas is not limited to birds. Large and small mammals such as white-tailed deer, opossums, raccoons, squirrels, striped skunks, and pocket gophers roam all over the Refuge. Two unusual mammals may also be seen at Aransas—the collared peccary (javelina) and the armadillo. The peccary is a secretive animal, easily provoked and quick to retaliate; it will not hesitate to attack human beings. The armadillo, on the other hand, is quite docile and curious; visitors to Aransas often find these peculiar animals underfoot.

Wildlife refuges not only protect and support mammals and birds, but provide for plants, insects, amphibians, and reptiles that are also becoming scarce. The intelligent management of a refuge entails the proper use of the land. A species in danger of extinction may be saved by simply providing a protected area which contains the type of habitat required by that species. Here, in the protected area, wildlife can feed, rest, and bear young. But in the case of a far-ranging species, such as the whooping crane, a refuge can only provide protection and habitat on a part-time basis.

Adequate food supplies are vital for the support of wildlife in a refuge, not only for the existing population, but for future generations. This calls for careful land management, with emphasis on a good ground cover. Overgrazed lands must be returned to native grasses and shrubs. Marshes and swamps must be restored to as close to their original condition as possible.

Various specialists cooperate in the management of a wildlife refuge. Dams, dikes, and fences are designed and built by engineers. Crops and other plant life are supervised by agronomists and botanists. Trees and shrubs come under the supervision of foresters. The regulation of livestock grazing programs in refuges is supervised by agronomists, soil conservation experts, and livestock specialists. Other specialists contribute to the management of a refuge.

Most refuges are an asset to a state and community, and contribute substantially to the local economy. By law, the local government shares in revenues from cooperative farming, sale of timber products, hay crops, grazing rights, and other by-products from the operation of a wildlife refuge.

Headquarters of the Aransas Refuge are located about eight miles southwest of Austwell, Texas, on highway 2-40. An observation tower stands southeast of the headquarters, overlooking Aransas Bay and Mustang Lake. Other observation platforms raised on twenty-foot poles have been set up on the outer edges of the Refuge. These are so situated that the territory between them can be scanned with binoculars. Refuge personnel check waterfowl and cranes by having one observer travel the intracoastal waterway in a boat, while the other observer goes from platform to platform by means of a car or truck. The observers can cover more territory in this manner and coordinate their observations by radio.

The whooping cranes wintering at Aransas are very wary and suspicious, quick to fly up and away when disturbed or alarmed. Therefore, their range is closed to visitors, since it is feared the cranes might abandon the Refuge for some other region less suitable for their way of living and protection. However, the visitor route extends to the edge of the whooper territory and a tower in a clump of trees provides an excellent view of the whooper habitat.

Besides human visitors, the whoopers also have to be protected from wolves, coyotes, snakes, and bobcats, all of which are potential hazards to them. To keep such predators away, a safety zone was created at Aransas that barred them from contact with the cranes.

The first accurate population count of the whooping cranes wintering in Aransas was initiated by James Stevenson, the manager of the Refuge, in the winter of 1938–39. In this census, eighteen whoopers were sighted on or near the Blackjack Peninsula.

Soon afterward a study of the cranes' feeding habits was inaugurated at Aransas. This was an especially important study, since information on the food and feeding habits of the cranes was scarce and unreliable. Not many persons had ever approached close enough to the birds for accurate observations. Farmers and ranchers living near the Aransas Refuge claimed the whoopers had raided sweet potato patches in past years, but Stevenson and John Lynch, a U.S. Fish and Wildlife Service biologist, only observed the whoopers eating clams, mullet, and burrowing crustaceans.

Meanwhile, in southwestern Louisiana in the 1930's, observers had counted ten whooping cranes. These cranes were divided into two groups: a coastal marsh flock and a prairie flock. It was thought that some, if not all, of the Louisiana whoopers remained in the region all year round, but this was mere speculation.

The Louisiana whoopers were entirely on their own, for there was no refuge in the region. Whooping cranes, as well as other wildlife, were unprotected and at the mercy of predatory men and animals. People living in the whooper region, mostly Cajuns (Acadian French), reported that the birds fed on blue crabs, crayfish, water insects, marsh-onion roots, prairie-lily bulbs, and sprouted corn. However, this dietary information was the total sum of knowledge on the cranes. Nothing else was known about their habits.

Sparse though it was, the data obtained from studies, observations, and reports in Texas and Louisiana helped fill out the dossier on the whooping cranes. Although there were still many gaps and omissions in the file, biologists were able to piece together a rough picture of the whooping crane's situation. By studying and collating all the data contributed over the years by explorers, fur traders, soldiers, map makers, bird painters, naturalists, conservationists, and biologists, a germ of a plan to save the whooping cranes slowly emerged.

But the threat of extinction moved closer in the 1940's when an unexpected disaster further reduced the small number of cranes. A hurricane roared in from the Atlantic and ripped through the gulf states. The Louisiana coastal marshes were especially hard hit, and all but one of the cranes disappeared from the region. This lone crane was captured and placed in the Audubon Park Zoo in New Orleans. Added to the calamity of the hurricane was the dismal news in 1944 that only one whooper had been sighted over Nebraska during migration.

This sudden turn for the worse in the plight of the whooping cranes aroused conservationists from their lethargy. The Bird Protection Committee of the American Ornithologists' Union issued a call for action. The Committee urged both the National Audubon Society and the U.S. Fish and Wildlife Service to take immediate steps to learn "the exact status of this species throughout its range and institute practical methods to forestall its extinction."

But what could be done? Calling for action was one thing; deciding on what that action should be was another. The preservation of the rare whooping cranes posed a very difficult problem. There was a lack of adequate information on the bird and its needs. Furthermore, complete "police" protection was not yet feasible, for the migration route was long and infiltrated by hunters. Finally, the nesting grounds were unknown. Nevertheless, the National Audubon Society and U.S. Fish and Wildlife Service agreed to pool their resources. They would investigate methods of halting—or at least decelerating—the whooping crane's rush into oblivion.

In 1945, the two organizations announced the creation of the Whooping Crane Project. They entered into a joint sponsorship of field investigations, research on numbers, location of the nesting grounds, and life history of the whooping crane. The first mission of the joint stewardship would be to search for the nesting grounds.

More than mere curiosity was involved in finding out

where the cranes nested. A knowledge of the location and character of the nesting grounds would provide biologists and others dedicated to the task of saving the whoopers with the answers to some vital questions. For instance, were the nesting grounds in danger of encroachment by land developers? When did the cranes arrive at the nesting site? How soon did they settle down to the job of incubating the eggs? What was the estimated incubation time? How soon did the young whoopers start flying? And what were the natural hazards present in the breeding grounds? These and other questions would have to be answered if the cranes and their problems were to be placed in the proper perspective.

The old records and reports showed that the whooping cranes had once nested in north-central United States, in open, flat, or slightly rolling country, interspersed with cattail, bulrush, and sedge marshes. The general character of the old nesting sites was what ecologists call "parkland," and many regions in North America—especially in Canada—still fitted this description and requirement.

Biologists more or less agreed that the unknown nesting grounds were probably in a wild, isolated region. Unlike the sandhill cranes which were often within shouting distance of human settlements, the whooping crane shunned civilization. Aloof, wary, and endowed with a strong sense of freedom, he sought the remote corners of the wilderness. His way of life demanded space and liberty, and he could not or would not adapt to a confined existence. As civilization crept closer, the whoopers simply retreated beyond the reach of man and his tendency to alter or modify nature.

But the nature detectives who were assigned to hunt for the whooper nests meant the birds no harm. The hunters were not despoilers, but conservationists, dedicated to the preservation and efficient supervision of our natural resources. And the whooping crane was one of the rarest of those resources.

THREE

The Hunt Begins—1945

The creation of the Whooping Crane Project was a giant step in the race to save the whoopers, and interested persons rejoiced in the fact that something concrete was being done at last. But it was apparent that the search for the nesting grounds would require the combined efforts of American and Canadian wildlife specialists. Fortunately, there was good rapport between the United States and Canada in matters concerning wildlife. The Migratory Bird Treaty, or Convention, of 1916 was an excellent example of past cooperation between the U.S. and Canadian governments for the conservation of wildlife indigenous to both countries.

The Treaty called for the mutual protection of waterfowl, insectivorous birds, and migratory non-game birds. Closed seasons, during which no hunting of the birds on the protected list would be permitted, were defined and established. Most important, a continuous closed season was established on the whooping and sandhill cranes. Other conditions of the Convention included the prohibition of nest or egg collection of protected birds, except for scientific or propagating purposes.

Canadian naturalists and conservationists were as aware as their colleagues in the U.S. of the need to protect and preserve the whooping cranes. And since the big cranes were part-time residents in Canada, the Canadian Wildlife Service had a strong interest in the hunt for the nesting grounds. The Service readily agreed to a three-way stewardship over the whoopers with the U.S. Fish and Wildlife Service and the National Audubon Society.

American and Canadian wildlife specialists participating in the Whooping Crane Project were under no illusions as to the enormity of the task confronting them. All signs pointed to a very difficult mission—especially the search for the nesting grounds.

John Dewey Soper, Chief Federal Migratory Bird Officer for the Canadian Prairie Provinces of Manitoba, Saskatchewan, and Alberta spelled out some of the difficulties that lay ahead of the nest hunters. First of all, the hunt would involve extensive travel over thousands of acres of Canadian wilderness north of the Great Plains. Some remote regions were accessible only by canoe or on foot. The hunters would have to course over swamps, swales, potholes, prairies, and in and out among countless lakes, ponds, and rivers. Since the hunt would have to be conducted in summer, there would be heat, flies, and mosquitoes to plague the hunters. Rivers jammed with logs and beaver dams would slow up the search. The men who hunted the whooper nests would need stamina and perseverance.

The search would be less rigorous and time-consuming if some potential nesting area could be designated beforehand. But nobody knew of such a site. Therefore, the search would require a large amount of good management, a generous portion of persistence, and a more than liberal share of good luck. Above all, the nest hunters would have to be tough, determined, and dedicated to the task. Locating a handful of birds in the immense Canadian wilderness was no job for armchair naturalists.

None of the organizations pledged to assist in the hunt could spare more than a few men. There could be no large posses beating the Canadian bush for whooper nests. Nor would squadrons of planes and helicopters be crisscrossing over the wilderness, with binocular-armed spotters leaning out of windows or cockpits. The hunt would have to be made by a few men who could be spared from other duties during the time the whooping cranes were in Canada.

It was decided that the Canadian Wildlife Service would take to the trail first. Before the actual search began, however, all past reports on the whoopers had to be reviewed, and likely nesting regions selected. Admittedly, the data were meager and much of the information unreliable. Yet every clue had to be examined and followed up, no matter how farfetched it might seem. It was also important to solicit new information on the migration of the cranes and the possible whereabouts of the nests. Acting on this idea, the leaders of the Whooping

Crane Project enlisted the aid of bird watchers and other interested persons to report sightings of whoopers after the cranes left Aransas in mid-April.

Since the cranes migrated over Texas, Oklahoma, Kansas, Nebraska, South Dakota, North Dakota, and then into Saskatchewan, it was decided that the plight of the whoopers and the work of the Project should be publicized in all these areas. But the initial publicity would be limited to the Canadian Prairie Provinces, where information on the birds was to be sent out to various organizations, agencies, groups, and individuals.

Charles L. Broley, a retired bank manager of Winnipeg, Manitoba, agreed to handle the publicity campaign. Broley was an enthusiastic and energetic naturalist, who achieved distinction some years later for his valuable studies of the bald eagle. He would have preferred to do actual field work on the whooping cranes, but was unable to at the time. Still, he knew he could make an important contribution to the search through his publicity efforts.

With his customary energy, Broley plunged into the chore of spreading information about the whooping cranes and soliciting reports on them. He circulated the material among agencies and individuals whose businesses and homes were located in areas most likely to harbor whooping cranes. All agreed to help. *The Prairie Farmer and Country Guide,* a magazine with a combined circulation in excess of 450,000 readers, promised to feature stories on the whooping cranes. It also invited readers to gather and send in any information they might have on the birds.

Ducks Unlimited, a sportsmen's group, asked its staff to

report any whooping crane observations. The Canadian Pacific Railways ran a story about the whooping crane, along with a photograph of the bird, in its company magazine. The Canadian Broadcasting Corporation devoted special broadcasts to the whooping crane and its plight. And the *Winnipeg Tribune,* a daily newspaper, gave considerable coverage in its columns to the Whooping Crane Project.

Fred Bard, Jr., Curator of the Provincial Museum of Natural History in Regina, Saskatchewan, joined the Whooping Crane Project for two months in the spring of 1945. Bard was the son of Fred Bard, Sr., who served with the Royal Northwest Mounted Police in many parts of the Canadian Northwest. Young Bard grew up in the region and had a wide knowledge of the country, its people and wildlife. In 1925, at the age of seventeen, Bard was hired by the Provincial Museum as a student preparator. He became one of the best qualified ornithologists in western Canada and was one of the first persons who recognized the need to accumulate data on the whooping cranes.

Bard's first job on the Whooping Crane Project was to collect, collate, and interpret reports on the cranes which came in as a result of Broley's publicity campaign. There were many reports and Bard spent considerable time in sifting through them. Next, he narrowed the field of search and selected a region most likely to contain the whoopers. The majority of reports indicated that the whoopers entered Saskatchewan from North Dakota and then disappeared. Negative as this evidence seemed, it was an important clue.

Sherlock Holmes, that astute detective of fiction, once

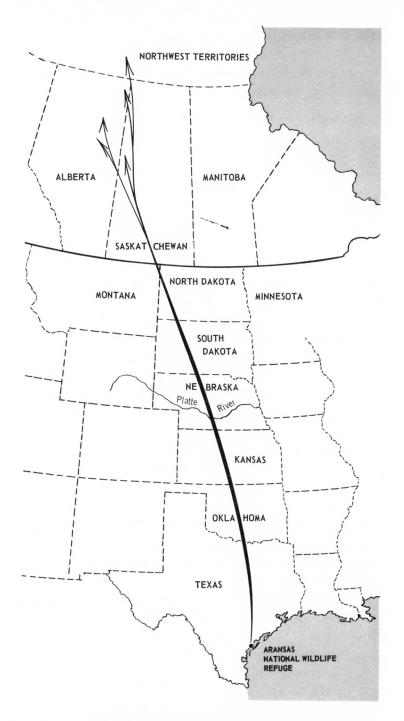

Migration Route of the Whooping Cranes

remarked to his friend and associate, Dr. Watson: "When you have eliminated all that is impossible, then whatever remains—however improbable—must be the truth. If several explanations remain, then one tries test after test until one or another of them has a convincing amount of support."

Bard heeded Holmes's advice. The United States was eliminated from the search plan because no whoopers had been known to nest there since possibly the beginning of the twentieth century. Eastern Canada also was ruled out, since no reports of whooping cranes had come in from that area. The last known whooper nest in Canada had been discovered at Muddy Lake, Saskatchewan, in 1922, and now many observers reported that the whooping cranes were entering Saskatchewan. Therefore, Bard decided that the evidence pointed to Saskatchewan, and neighboring Manitoba and Alberta, as the most likely sites.

Since he was to conduct the initial search for the nests, Bard needed a definite starting point. He settled on Saskatchewan and eastern Alberta. Accordingly, he plotted four potential search areas on his map. *Number one* was a region in southeastern Alberta, north of a town with the odd name of Medicine Hat. Search area *number two* was to be east-central Saskatchewan, beyond Nipawin. *Number three* would be in central Saskatchewan beyond Meadow Lake; and *number four*, the settled region west of Saskatoon.

Why were the Prairie Provinces selected as likely regions for the whooping cranes? There were three sound reasons: (1) Manitoba, Saskatchewan, and Alberta con-

tained vast wilderness areas which could meet the re-
quirements of the whooping cranes; (2) historical data
showed that whoopers had been sighted in these three
provinces; and (3) recent reports stated that the cranes
entered Saskatchewan after migrating north from Aransas.

While Saskatchewan seemed the most likely region to
start the hunt, Bard had to consider the possibility of the
whoopers fanning out to other Prairie Provinces after entering Saskatchewan from the United States. The big
cranes might very well travel east to Manitoba or west to
Alberta, possibly even into British Columbia, although
that province was mountainous.

Manitoba is the most eastern of the Canadian Prairie
Provinces. It lies in three distinct physiographic regions:
the Hudson Bay Lowlands, Canadian Shield, and Interior
Plains. Only a relatively small area of northeastern Manitoba is in the Hudson Bay Lowlands. It is a region composed of surface gravel, rock, and bog. The eastern, central, and northern sections of the province are part of the
Canadian Shield. Much of this region is covered by gla-
cially deposited clay gravel, rock, and bog. Southwestern
Manitoba is a soil-covered region in the Interior Plains. It
is a fertile area and settlement is heaviest in this part of
the province, which is a great wheat-growing section.

The Manitoba plains were once a part of the bed of a
huge glacial lake called Lake Agassiz by geologists. This
enormous glacial lake spread over southern Manitoba and
part of eastern Saskatchewan, and extended into the
United States, in what is today the Dakotas and Minnesota. The Lake of the Woods in northern Minnesota is a

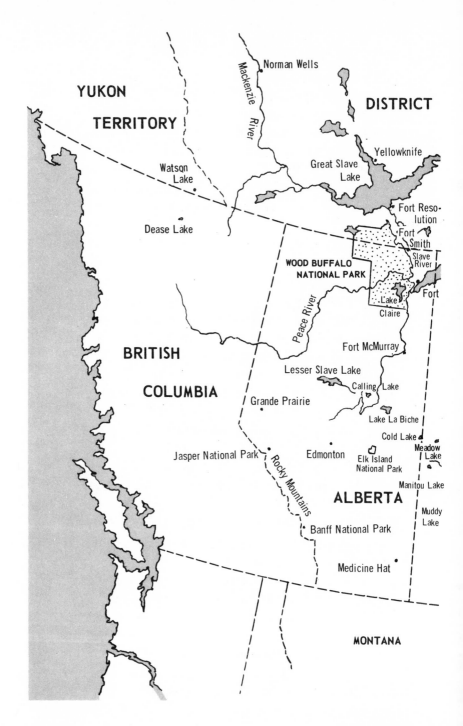

The Canadian

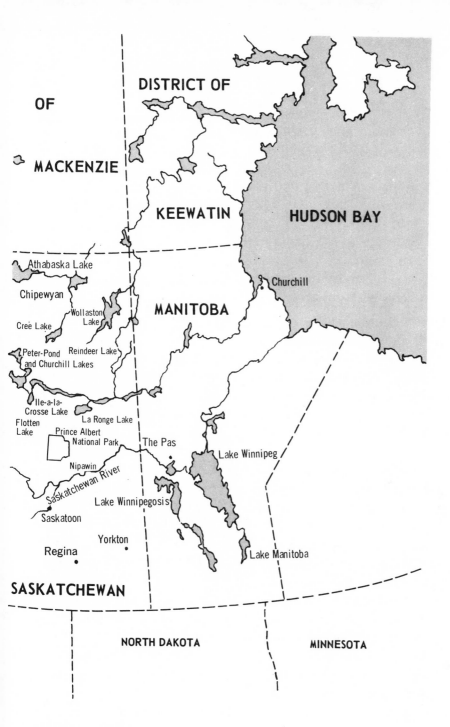

Prairie Provinces

remnant of this great prehistoric lake. Geologists estimate that Lake Agassiz was more than 700 miles long and 250 miles wide.

Manitoba is a land of countless waterways. The Central Plain has three extremely large lakes: Winnipeg, Manitoba, and Winnipegosis. Three major rivers flow into Lake Winnipeg—the Saskatchewan, the Winnipeg, and the Red. The many basins of the Canadian Shield region of Manitoba contain hundreds of small lakes and ponds.

Thousands of waterfowl, especially mallards, canvasbacks, and Canadian geese, dot the lakes, ponds, and rivers of Manitoba. Black bears, moose, elk, and deer roam the forests, fields, and wetlands. Smaller mammals, including rabbits, squirrels, weasels, and other fur-bearing animals, go about the endless task of food hunting and rearing young.

While Bard did not consider Manitoba a prime search area, he did not ignore the possibilities of this province as a haven for the whooping cranes. He knew from Samuel Hearne's journals that the whoopers once nested near Churchill at Hudson Bay in the northeast corner of the province. Also, one or two whoopers had been reported in the area in recent years. This was too important a clue to be rejected without investigation.

Next door to and west of Manitoba is Saskatchewan, a province that is larger than any European country. Its area is greater than the combined acreage of South Dakota, North Dakota, and Nebraska. The average distance east to west in Saskatchewan is 335 miles; the north to south measurement is 761 miles.

Saskatchewan lies between the Interior Plains and Ca-

nadian Shield. The northern third of the province—
which forms part of the Shield—is marked by glaciation,
erosion, and a generally rough landscape. There are bare
and exposed outcroppings of rock, thin soil, and muskeg,
with here and there a sandy patch or knoll. The lakes,
rivers, muskegs, sandy patches, and knolls all intermingle
to produce a wild, chaotic pattern of wilderness. Saskatchewan's four largest lakes are in the northern part of the
province. These are Lake Athabaska (one third of which
is in the next province, Alberta), Reindeer Lake, Wollas-
ton, and La Ronge.

The southern part of Saskatchewan is in sharp contrast
to the northern. It is a rolling plain, sloping slightly to
the north, with extensive stretches that are open, grassy,
and relatively treeless. Human settlement has been limited largely to this region, scarcely reaching beyond a
point 350 miles north of the Saskatchewan–United States
border. It is one of the centers of the Canadian wheat-
farming community.

Saskatchewan is drained in a generally northeastern
direction toward Hudson Bay. Three important rivers
make up the main drainage system. The Churchill River
and its tributaries drain the northern section of the province. In the southeast, the Assiniboine River and two
tributaries, the Qu'Appelle and Souris, flow into Nelson
River and Hudson Bay. And the great Saskatchewan
River drains most of the plains in the central and southern regions.

The Saskatchewan River, which the native Indians
called the "Kisiskatchewan," is the Mississippi of the
Prairie Provinces. The first white man to see it was Henry

Kelsey, a fur trader with the Hudson's Bay Company, who reached its banks in 1690.

Carrying water from the Canadian Rockies, the Saskatchewan rolls through hundreds of miles of the central plains in a large, undulating Y designated as the north and south branches. The river is always well below the surface of the prairies and rarely overflows its banks. In summer, when the water level drops, sand bars thrust upward in the channels. Weeds and wild flowers cloak the banks where the river slices its way through the endless sea of grass. It is a lonely river, but a haven for waterfowl and fur-bearing animals in a desolate region of land, sky, and water.

Saskatchewan is a wonderland of wildlife. Two of North America's bird flyways—the Mississippi and the Central—converge over it. The province has one of the highest concentrations of migratory waterfowl in the world. Shore or wading birds ring the perimeters of thousands of ponds and potholes. Upland game birds are plentiful in both the northern and southern portions of the province. Big game animals include moose, elk, white-tailed and mule deer, antelope, and caribou. Thousands of smaller mammals and birds are also permanent residents.

With its innumerable bogs, swamps, marshes, potholes, plains, rivers, lakes and ponds, Saskatchewan certainly seemed a promising area in the hunt for the whooping cranes. Bard intended to make a thorough search of selected areas in the province, running down every clue.

His search plans also called for an inspection of a region in southeastern Alberta, the most westerly of the Prairie

Provinces. Alberta stretches 300 miles from east to west and 800 miles from north to south. Almost all of the province is upland prairie—a part of the Interior Plains. The extreme northeastern tip of Alberta, near Lake Athabaska, is part of the Canadian Shield.

Alberta's physiography changes abruptly in the southwestern section. This region is in the Rocky Mountains and is part of the Canadian Cordillera, a main mountain range of North America. About a million years ago, the snows on these mountains remained all year and formed great glaciers. In the northwestern Canadian Rockies, the ice formed a single sheet. Extending out from this vast ice sheet were the glaciers which moved southward down the Rockies and the Cascade-Sierra ranges. Some of the North American continent's highest and most majestic peaks are in southeastern Alberta and the neighboring province of British Columbia.

While most of southern and central Alberta is composed of plains, there are relief sections of hills. Elevations in the province rise from 600 feet along the Slave River in the northeast to 2,000 to 4,000 feet in the plains. The largest slice of the province lies in the Athabaska, Peace, and Hay river basins. These basins all drain into the Arctic Sea by way of the Slave and Mackenzie rivers. Alberta shares Lake Athabaska and Cold Lake with Saskatchewan. Other large lakes in Alberta include Lakes Claire and Lesser Slave, and Lac la Biche. Like its sister province Saskatchewan, Alberta teems with wildlife.

When all of the physiographic features of the Prairie Provinces were evaluated, especially the waterways and muskeg regions, it appeared that the hunt for the whooper nests could be narrowed to these three portions of Canada. The Prairie Provinces had the kind of wilderness preferred by the big cranes and were similar in many respects to the wintering grounds at Aransas.

Once the search plans were completed, Fred Bard readied himself for the field. The National Audubon Society contributed a collapsible canoe, outboard motor, and a tent. Bard's strategy, or plan of operation, called for flights to specific search areas, setting up base camps, and then scouting the surrounding territories for signs of the whooping cranes. He was authorized to promptly arrange for warden protection for any whoopers or nests he might discover.

The whooping cranes had long since left Aransas when Bard started out on the first leg of the search, in the late spring of 1945.

*   *   *

Deep in the Canadian wilderness, the whooping cranes staked out their nesting territories. The urge to mate was strong within them. Two whoopers, lately arrived at the nesting grounds, hurried into their prenuptial dance on the shore of a pond. The male moved his red-patched head up and down, long neck gracefully outstretched. He flapped his wings back and forth rapidly. Then, pushing off with stiffened legs, he leaped three feet into the air. While in the air he flung back his glossy head, so that his beak pointed skyward like a sharp reed.

The crane's long neck arched over his back. Up and down he bounced, stiltlike legs striking the ground with a jarring force. And all the while he leaped, his powerful wings fanned the air, black tips gleaming like shiny coal.

Now the female joined in the ritual. She ran forward a few paces, head bobbing to and fro, wings flapping with intense excitement. Up and down she leaped, almost in unison with the dancing male. Leap followed leap. Faster and faster jumped the cranes. Neither uttered a sound.

Suddenly the female stopped leaping. She crouched forward, head bowed in a graceful gesture of supplication. Her wings were thrust away from her body, black tips spread apart and pointing downward. The male ran eagerly toward her, his wings held aloft. Then he sprang up from the ground in a mighty leap and sailed over the female's posturing body.

Now the mating dance was over. Safe in their wilderness retreat, far from the prying eyes of civilization, the cranes began the important task of building their nests. Soon, if all went well, there would be chicks to feed and guard from danger.

*   *   *

Arrangements were made for Fred Bard to fly on nest-hunting trips with the Search and Rescue Group of the United States Air Force. World War II was still in progress and units of the American Air Force were sta-

tioned in parts of Alaska and Canada. The Commanding
General of the U.S. Air Force based in Regina, the capital
of Saskatchewan, authorized Bard to fly on "familiarization flights." One of these flights would soon leave Watson
Lake in the Yukon. The exact route of the flight was not
known, but Bard suggested that perhaps the plane could
be routed over Saskatchewan eastward to The Pas on the
Saskatchewan–Manitoba border. This area was included
in his search plan. But his request was turned down; no
authorization could be given for planes to fly over Saskatchewan.

Bard flew from Regina to Watson Lake in the Yukon
Territory, just over the northern border of British
Columbia. Again he attempted to induce U.S. Air Force
personnel to fly him over some of his search areas. He
met with sympathetic listeners, but no offers to fly him
over Saskatchewan were made. It seemed that nobody at
Watson Lake had the authority or wanted to take the
responsibility for sending planes off their scheduled flight
patterns.

Shortly after his arrival at Watson Lake, Bard took off
on one of the familiarization flights. The plane's destination was Dease Lake in northern British Columbia,
and Bard had an exciting and interesting flight. The
landscape over which he flew is breath-taking, with
rough, purple valleys, deep canyons, glaciers, lakes and
ponds. But it was strictly a sight-seeing trip. There were
no whooping cranes in the mountains. Furthermore, the
pilot navigated the plane through mountain passes at an
altitude between 5,000 and 7,000 feet. Bard couldn't
have spotted a whooping crane from this altitude, even

if they had been in the region. Besides, British Columbia was not one of the designated search areas; nobody had reported whoopers in this province.

Stymied though he was for a means of flying over his chosen areas, Bard kept on the trail of the whoopers. He cornered trappers, hunters, Mounties, and anyone whom he thought might have information on the whereabouts of the cranes. But all he obtained were guesses and outdated reports on white birds that sounded very much like snow geese.

After his fruitless trip to Watson Lake, Bard returned to Edmonton, the capital and largest city in Alberta. Located in the north-central part of the province on the north branch of the Saskatchewan River, Edmonton is a major business, industrial, and mixed-farming center, and is steeped in fur trade history and lore. Fort Edmonton, a Hudson's Bay Company post, was built high on the left bank of the Saskatchewan. For many years it was the dominant trading post in the valley, even though the rival fur company, The Northwest Company, erected Fort Augustus nearby.

Settlers came into the Edmonton region in 1873, and a year later the Royal Canadian Mounted Police moved in to bring law and order. By the year 1879, the settlement had spread beyond the palisades of Fort Edmonton. A land boom brought new settlers rushing in from all over Canada. The town began to flourish and by 1883 the Edmonton school boasted of forty pupils. In the gold rush of 1898, eager prospectors outfitted in Edmonton and then mushed on to the supposed gold lodes in the Yukon. Many hungry, empty-handed, and disillusioned gold seekers returned to Edmonton and made their homes in the town, which now consisted of 3,000 citizens.

When Fred Bard stopped off in Edmonton in 1945, this historical city had a population of nearly 300,000. It was the capital of a great province, the seat of the University of Alberta, gateway to the Peace River country and all the fur and mineral wealth of the Mackenzie–Athabaska region.

In Edmonton, Bard again communicated with the Commanding General of the U.S. Air Force. The general agreed with Bard that flying at a height of 5,000 or more feet was not very helpful in spotting whooping cranes on the ground. He told Bard that the next flight would be more suitable. But there was no next flight. The U.S. Air Force made no more offers to fly Bard around on his search for the whooping cranes. No reasons were given for the withdrawal of help, but it was obvious that national security and other complications prohibited this kind of unrestricted flying over Canadian territory. Bard would have to look elsewhere for air transportation.

Since it was now June 30th, Bard decided to abandon his search in Alberta and to follow up some leads in Saskatchewan. He departed from Edmonton and went back to Regina, where he had begun his unsuccessful journeying.

While Bard was having his troubles finding someone to fly him around, the U.S. Fish and Wildlife Service sent Robert H. Smith, a Flyway biologist and waterfowl specialist, out on the hunt for the whooper nests. At this time, Smith, a ten-year veteran of the Service, was stationed in Winona, Minnesota. He was a graduate of Dartmouth

College, with a major in biology, including zoology, botany, and geology.

His duties as Mississippi Flyway biologist involved research in developing techniques for the measurement of waterfowl populations during fall migrations, on wintering grounds, and in breeding areas. Smith had developed the Arctic waterfowl survey technique used by both American and Canadian personnel. He had also learned to fly at his own expense and was assigned a plane by the U.S. Fish and Wildlife Service in 1945. An experienced hunter, fisherman, canoeist, and pilot, he was one of the Service's top field men.

Smith flew up to Alberta in a Grumman Widgeon used for waterfowl population surveys. He scouted the territory between the Athabaska and Pembina rivers northwest of Edmonton, a region dotted with lakes and ponds. He saw hundreds of ducks and other waterfowl, but no whooping cranes.

Bard joined Smith, and the two biologists traveled to Nipawin in northeastern Saskatchewan, one of the areas Bard thought might contain whoopers. Nipawin, a small town of about 3,800 people, is located on the north branch of the Saskatchewan River. It is a rich agricultural center. The country around Nipawin is mostly aspen groves in the north; grasslands in the south. Farther north are vast stretches of conifer forests interspersed with lakes and ponds—an ideal waterfowl habitat. Bard and Smith coursed over this region by car and plane. They traveled 1,000 miles by car alone, keeping a constant vigilance for signs of whooping cranes. But they found none.

Now time ran out. Bard had to return to the Provincial

Museum in Regina, and Smith to his regular duties as Flyway biologist. Thus ended the first year of the hunt.

*　　*　　*

That fall, when the first icy breath of winter blew down from the Arctic, the whooping cranes winged toward the Texas gulf coast. Once again, they ran the hazardous gauntlet of the migration route to reach their wintering grounds. And they brought three youngsters along with them.

FOUR

The Second Attempt—1946

Naturally, the failure to locate even one whooping crane on the first hunt was a disappointment to Bard, Smith, and others concerned with the Whooping Crane Project. Of course it had been pointed out that the chances of quickly finding the whooper nests were slim. But still everyone had hoped that Bard and Smith would be lucky the first time out.

When Fred Bard's leave of absence ended, he returned to piled-up work at the Provincial Museum in Regina. Now it was necessary to find a replacement for him, and John H. Baker, President of the National Audubon Society, began to look around for a likely candidate. Baker, a dedicated naturalist and conservationist, was a key figure in the conception and establishment of the Whooping Crane Project. He was a tireless worker; energetic and willing to go all out for the Project. To replace Bard, Baker sought an experienced biologist, preferably an ornithologist with the stamina to endure weeks of rigorous coursing over and through the Canadian prairies, wilderness, and waterways. Fortunately, Baker knew of such a man: Dr. Olin Sewall Pettingill, Jr., then Associate Professor of Zoology at Carleton College, Northfield, Minnesota.

Dr. Pettingill was an outstanding ornithologist who had studied birds from the Arctic to the tropics, and the zones in between. The National Audubon Society originally hired him as a research fellow in the fall of 1945, but the teaching position at Carleton College came along about the same time, and Pettingill asked to be released from the Whooping Crane Project. However, in the spring of 1946, he found that he could devote further time to the Project.

While he was working for the Audubon Society in 1945, Pettingill familiarized himself with the whooping crane situation. He began his research in the museum and library at the University of Michigan, where he set about accumulating all available information on the birds, and went over the nesting and migration records. At the same time, he prepared a poster on the crane, illustrated by Dr. Walter J. Breckenridge. The poster showed a whooping crane, together with other birds which were often mistaken for the whooper. It was distributed by the U.S. Fish and Wildlife Service, and was displayed in post offices and other public buildings in all the states over which the cranes flew in their annual migrations.

Pettingill's next mission involved a visit to Fred Bard in Regina. The two biologists discussed the negative results of the first search, and examined new reports and other information on the elusive cranes. Both men were eager for another search the following summer, but both agreed that there was a lot of work to be done before a second search could be made.

After his conference with Bard, Dr. Pettingill went down to Aransas in the fall of 1945. He planned on studying the whoopers in their wintering grounds in the hope that he might turn up some clue that would lead to the nesting sites. One of his proposed projects at Aransas was a study of the whooping crane's feeding habits. Even if this study failed to produce any clues, the knowledge gained would add to the meager fund of data on the crane's life history.

Two methods of observing the feeding habits were used by Pettingill and the Aransas biologists. The first involved direct observation of the birds as they fed in the sloughs. This did not prove very satisfactory, however, because the biologists could not approach close enough to really see what the cranes ate. The birds were extremely wary and took to the air whenever anyone came too near them. The use of a blind was not always helpful, either. The cranes often simply walked away from it, out of range of the observers. Also, the biologists had no way of knowing just where to set up the blind on any given day. The cranes had no set time or pattern of activity and wandered over a wide territory. The other method of analyzing the intake of food involved an examination of the birds' droppings.

It was learned that the whoopers did not feed in flocks. Nor did they roost in a group, as was the custom of the

Whooping crane feeding
by Allan D. Cruickshank, from National Audubon Society

more numerous sandhill cranes. The whoopers were more individualistic, preferring to feed and roost in small family units or pairs. These would stake out a territory and rarely stray outside it. Usually there was enough food within the invisible boundaries of the territory to carry the pair or family over the winter.

The observations at Aransas by Pettingill and Refuge biologists revealed that the main diet of the whoopers consisted of blue crabs, marine worms, and mud shrimp. While this information was an important addition to the whooping crane's dossier, there were still some gaps in the knowledge of the feeding habits of the cranes. For example, what did they eat while on migration? And what did they consume at the unknown breeding grounds?

Past records showed that the cranes alighted on sand bars and mud flats in the rivers flowing across the migratory route. The big birds had been observed feeding in grain stubble fields, too, possibly on grain sprouts. They also had access to frogs, toads, fish, crayfish, young snakes, and turtles along the migration route, but nobody had actually observed them eating these potential foods.

About the middle of March, 1946, after he had rejoined the Project, Dr. Pettingill made a trip to New Orleans, where two captive whooping cranes were residing in the Audubon Park Zoo. One whooper had been captured in Nebraska, the other in Louisiana. Both birds had suffered injuries and it was considered inadvisable to release them in the wild, where they would be severely handicapped and unable to adequately defend themselves.

Aviculturists at the Audubon Park Zoo were interested in starting a captive flock of whooping cranes. The sex of

the two injured cranes was not known, but the aviculturists were hopeful that the pair would turn out to be
male and female. If so, it might be possible to breed them
and raise their chicks in captivity. Pettingill spent his time
at the Audubon Park Zoo observing the two captive
cranes, and then, as the spring migration time drew near,
he hurried back to Aransas.

By mid-April, the whoopers were well on their way to
Canada. Dr. Pettingill followed the migration route from
Texas through Oklahoma, Kansas, Nebraska, and the
Dakotas. He remained for a while in the Nebraska–Dakota region, conducting aerial searches along the Platte
River and other likely resting places, but did not see any
cranes. After this field work, Pettingill decided that another search for the nesting grounds should be made in
Saskatchewan and Alberta during the coming summer
months. With this rough plan in mind, he proceeded on
up to Regina, where he again met with Fred Bard.

The plans for the second hunt included a much more
extensive publicity campaign than that which had pre-
ceded the first one. Hunters were warned not to shoot
down any whooping cranes or any large birds resembling
them. This was a very important precaution, for there was
no way of knowing how many whoopers had been blasted
out of the skies in the past.

Pettingill's whooping crane poster was circulated in the
hope that hunters would see it and avoid shooting the big
cranes. Most were cooperative and promised to take a
good look before aiming at any large white bird, but there
was a hard core who didn't care what kind of bird they
shot as long as they hit their targets. This minority of men

and boys with guns and itchy trigger fingers had to be reached somehow. It was no easy task.

Fred Bard volunteered to supervise the new publicity campaign. Seven thousand questionnaires and posters on the whooping cranes were prepared for his use, and he distributed this material to 5,500 schools in Saskatchewan, eastern Alberta, and western Manitoba. The response was extremely heartening. Bard found that school teachers and children alike were vitally interested in wildlife and thrilled with the knowledge that they might be of some help in conserving and protecting the rare cranes.

Bard also sent the publicity material to radio stations, local newspapers, and approximately 500 members of the Yorkton, Saskatchewan, Natural History Society. The mailings also went to the Northwest Mounted Police, Hudson's Bay Company, Bureau of Indian Affairs, and other Canadian organizations and agencies. All of them promised to distribute the material among their agents and employees.

This publicity campaign proved to be a valuable prelude to the second hunt for the nesting grounds. For one thing, it turned the spotlight on the whooping cranes and their desperate situation. People who had never seen or heard of the big birds now expressed interest in their plight. The army being raised for the whooping cranes grew larger every day.

It was true that the bulk of the volunteer spotters were amateur naturalists and bird watchers, some of whose reports and data would no doubt prove inaccurate and generally unreliable. Past experience showed that not

only the route followed by the cranes had been errone-
ously reported, but the number of birds sighted as well.
None of the errors were intentional, of course. It wasn't
easy to identify a high-flying crane. And it was simple
to confuse greater and lesser sandhill cranes with whoopers, especially at a distance.

Naturally, there are differences between the sandhills
and whoopers. The adult sandhill crane is gray over-all
with the color lighter and ranging to a bluish-gray on the
neck. Sandhill heads have a bare cap that is bluish-pink,
with a few black hairs, while adult whoopers have a
scarlet-capped head. At close sighting, the differences between the whooper and sandhill are quite apparent. But
far away, one is easily mistaken for the other.

The chances were also good that an exaggerated number of whoopers would be reported by the volunteer spotters, who might see the same crane more than once. But
these errors could not be helped. If the whoopers were to
be saved and their nesting grounds discovered, no assistance—whether amateur or professional—could be
scorned or disregarded.

Dr. Pettingill was anxious to start the second hunt. Like
Bard before him, he selected promising search areas in
Saskatchewan and Alberta, the two provinces most likely
to hide the whooping cranes. Once the search plans were
drawn up, Pettingill was ready for the field. His wife,
Eleanor, joined him in Regina on June 6th and they drove
to Edmonton in Alberta. From Edmonton, the Pettingills
flew by commercial plane up to Fort McMurray at the
juncture of the Athabaska and Clearwater rivers in northeastern Alberta, and then went eastward to Waterways, a

small settlement on the Clearwater. There they awaited
the arrival of a U.S. Fish and Wildlife plane which was to
fly Pettingill farther north to a search area.

The Pettingills waited impatiently for the plane. But
they were disappointed when it finally arrived at Waterways, for it was equipped with wheels instead of floats.
Wheels were useless in that country pockmarked with
hundreds of lakes and ponds; floats or pontoons were absolutely necessary in case of emergency landings. Furthermore, the pilot had no emergency equipment, so he
wasn't keen on the job to start with. After some discussion, the pilot decided against flying Pettingill on his
search for the cranes and he took off, leaving the Pettingills at Waterways.

This was a serious and unexpected hitch in plans, since
Pettingill couldn't conduct much of a search without a
plane. He remained grounded until Dr. Terris Moore,
President of the New England Museum of Natural History, and his wife flew up from Boston in their private
plane. Together Pettingill and Moore made several trips
from Fort McMurray, flying a total of twenty-one and a
half hours over remote areas in Alberta and Saskatchewan. On one trip they flew eastward from McMurray
across Alberta by way of Gordon and Garson lakes, Peter
Pond and Churchill lakes.

Peter Pond, adjacent to and just west of Churchill
Lake, was named after a Connecticut fur trader and sol-
dier of fortune who was instrumental in extending the fur
trade into regions remote from the St. Lawrence country.
Pond was the first white man to visit the Athabaska River.
He also introduced the white man to pemmican, the In-

dian food composed of dried meat that was pounded fine and packed into sacks of hide. Pemmican seemed like an excellent emergency or "field ration" to Pond. He initiated the system of storing it along the banks of rivers for the use of the fur traders and voyageurs, or French-Canadian canoemen.

Interesting as Peter Pond was as a historic site, Pettingill and Moore saw no whooping cranes in the vicinity of the lake. They flew northeast into the Canadian Shield country around Cree Lake, where they discovered hundreds of waterfowl, but no whoopers. Turning south, they headed for Ile-a-la-Crosse, a many-coved lake southeast of Peter Pond. Again, no whoopers were sighted, and Pettingill and Moore cut west and north to McCusker, Watapi, and Graham lakes in Alberta. The story was the same there: no whooping cranes. The disappointed hunters flew back to McMurray, where some interesting news awaited them.

They were told that someone had sighted whooping cranes at Fort Chipewyan on Lake Athabaska. Pettingill and Moore quickly took off for the lake, and Mrs. Pettingill and Mrs. Moore followed a few days later in a commercial plane that made a weekly run up to Fort Chipewyan. But when the biologists tracked down the report on the whoopers, they found it to be three years old. Besides, there was no certainty that the birds sighted by the observer had been whooping cranes. Nevertheless, Pettingill and Moore, unwilling to neglect even a negative clue such as this one, made a trip along the southern end of Lake Athabaska, circling the entire area for signs of whoopers. Finding none, they went on down to Lake

Claire by way of the Athabaska River and made a complete circuit of that lake. They sighted hundreds of ducks and geese, but not one whooping crane.

The weary hunters flew back to Fort Chipewyan. Time was running out for Dr. Moore, and he had also exhausted his limited supply of gasoline. The search was ended for him, at least for that year. He and Mrs. Moore took leave of the Pettingills and flew off to Boston in their small Taylor-craft plane. When the Moores left, Olin and Eleanor Pettingill were more or less stranded in Fort Chipewyan, an Indian center with a Hudson's Bay Company post. Since they had no means of transportation, all they could do was wait for help or instructions. But there was no word from either the National Audubon Society or the U.S. Fish and Wildlife Service. Everyone seemed to have forgotten them.

While they waited, the Pettingills decided to camp north of Fort Chipewyan. Just west of Lake Athabaska is a great marshy region formed by the combined delta of the Peace and Athabaska rivers. It is a wild, remote area, miles from civilization, and there had been some vague reports that whoopers nested in the great marsh.

The Pettingills moved into the marsh area and set up a camp, where they intended to stay until they received further instructions. Early one morning they were routed out of bed by the sound of loud gunfire popping all around them. The startled campers thrust their heads out of the tent to see what all the shooting was about, and saw a band of Indians gliding past in canoes, and merrily firing their guns into the air.

This was shortly after the 1st of July, when the Canadian Government usually paid the Indians "treaty money"—about $5.00 apiece. The Indians were celebrating the big event. They had gone to Fort Chipewyan to receive their money, which they promptly invested in ammunition. Now they were on the way home, shooting away their bonuses as they paddled their canoes through the great marsh.

The Pettingills decided then and there that no whooping cranes were likely to be nesting in that marsh or vicinity. But where were the big birds?

*   *   *

That summer there were three new whooping cranes in the secret hideaway. The young cranes were now four months old and nearly four feet high, with cinnamon-colored bodies. Here and there, patches of baby down still clung to their breasts. The young cranes had big heads that bristled with new russet feathers. Their feet looked too big for their bodies, as if the youngsters were wearing oversized shoes.

The sun was warm and the young cranes darted back and forth in the shallow water of the pond. They could find and catch their own food now and carefully searched for snails, tadpoles, minnows, and waterbugs. On the land, the ungainly youngsters raced after butterflies and other winged insects, their big feet clomping over the ground. They were very vocal at times, piercing the stillness of the marshes with screechy calls, reminiscent of the changing voices of adolescent boys.

Alert parents, their red-topped heads flashing in the July sun, kept watchful eyes on the gamboling youngsters. The big cranes never relaxed their vigilance day or night, for the wilderness was filled with danger. Death could dive down out of the skies in the speeding form of a bald eagle or lightning-fast peregrine falcon. Or a hungry fox might lurk behind a bush, patiently waiting for an unsuspecting young crane to wander past.

The summer lazed along and the young cranes grew taller and taller. They had prodigious appetites, eating almost everything they found. It was a good thing that they did, for in a short time they would have to make the long and strenuous journey to Aransas.

But, like all youngsters, the immature cranes had no thought of tomorrow. Life for them was here, today, in the Canadian wilderness. And they had fun dabbling in the ponds, dashing in and out among the reeds and sedges, and bouncing over hummocks after insects. When they tired of these activities, the young cranes tried their wings, skimming over the ground, half-flying, half-leaping in their awkward attempts to become airborne.

At night, the tired youngsters sought shelter and comfort from the cool air by snuggling against the warm bodies of their parents. They listened to the night cries that echoed eerily over the marshes, and then they went to sleep. And all through the night the big cranes dozed, unaware that civilization was creeping closer and closer to their secret nesting grounds.

*   *   *

Toward the end of July, Bob Smith of the U.S. Fish and Wildlife Service flew up to Fort Chipewyan, and he and Pettingill flew another twenty and a half hours over prairies and wetlands in the search for the whooping cranes. So far, there was not a single trace of the birds, not even a lost feather. Nor were there any reports of anybody else sighting whoopers. The cranes had been swallowed up by the wilderness.

During a three-day period, from July 23 to 26, Pettingill and Smith flew over the junction of the Athabaska and Pembina rivers, northwest of Edmonton. This was the region containing large numbers of waterfowl which Smith had scouted in 1945. The Athabaska River is the southernmost tributary of the mighty Mackenzie River. It rises in the ice fields of the Canadian Rockies, trickling down off Mt. Columbia, north of Banff National Park near the British Columbia border. Gathering size and strength, the Athabaska flows north from Mt. Columbia and on up through Jasper National Park, where it swings northeast and courses on to Edmonton. Its total length, from Mt. Columbia to Lake Athabaska, is 765 miles. Oil sands along this river are thought to be among the world's largest petroleum reserves.

Finding no cranes around the confluence of the Athabaska and Pembina rivers, the two biologists inspected the region around Calling Lake, and then flew northwest to Lesser Slave Lake. They traveled along the southern boundary of this lonely body of water and continued west to Grande Prairie, crossing over the Smoky River. They were now close to the British Columbia boundary. Here they examined the region near the Wapiti River, which flows through Saskatoon Provincial Park slightly to the south of Grande Prairie.

There were plenty of ducks and geese to be seen, but no whooping cranes. Smith swung the plane around on a southeasterly course and headed for North Battleford, Kerrobert, and Manitou Lake over in Saskatchewan, flying along the southern rim of Lesser Slave Lake on the way. While on this leg of their search, Pettingill and Smith visited Muddy Lake, the site of the last known whooping crane nest. But they met with disappointment there. The old whooping crane nesting site was dried up, and there were no signs that indicated the big cranes ever returned to this region.

Time was running out for Pettingill and he had to give up the search. He and Mrs. Pettingill returned to New York. Smith, flying solo, logged another 126½ hours while making a routine census of waterfowl on the lakes, ponds, and wetlands of Alberta and Saskatchewan. His flights carried him over great tracts of wild and desolate country, including much of the prairie and aspen parkland. He also scouted the bush country around Lac la Biche in Alberta. After exhausting this region, Smith flew around the perimeter of Prince Albert National Park in north-central Saskatchewan.

Prince Albert Park was a likely region for whooping cranes, since it had many of the environmental features needed by the birds. More important, whoopers had been reported in this area in the latter part of the nineteenth century. The cranes had also been reported at Meadow Lake, due west of Prince Albert Park, and in the Nipawin area, southeast of the park, as late as 1944.

Established in 1927, and located in the central section of Saskatchewan, about 100 miles north of the city of Saskatoon, Prince Albert Park is the fourth largest of the Canadian National Parks. All of its 1,496 square miles of acreage lies within the lush conifer tree belt north of the wheatlands of the Great Plains. Certainly there was ample room for the handful of whooping cranes in this great preserve.

For the most part, Prince Albert Park is an extensive region of rolling hills, ridges, countless lakes, ponds, streams, bogs, and marshes. The rippling hills and ridges are coated with evergreen trees. In the drier portions, the commonest tree is the white spruce, occasionally found mixed with balsam fir and jack pine. Quaking aspen is abundant in the cleared areas, and there are thick stands of black spruce, larch, and balsam poplar in the wet sections. Around the margins of the lakes, ponds, and bogs grow large clumps of reeds and sedges.

Prince Albert Park teems with wildlife. Large mammals include the gray wolf, elk, black bear, white-tailed deer, and, in the northern sections, woodland caribou. A small herd of American bison is kept in a fenced area near the entrance to the park. Smaller mammals are the varying hare, Canada porcupine, skunk, beaver, red fox, red squirrel, Canada lynx, coyote, and marten. Badger and pocket gophers live in the prairie-like areas of the park.

This great park shelters 174 species of birds. Its large

number of lakes and ponds provide excellent habitats for all kinds of waterfowl. Mallard, blue-winged teal, common loon, red-necked grebe, shoveller, ring-necked duck, herring gull, common tern, great blue heron, marsh hawk (harrier), red-tailed hawk, bald eagle, and osprey live within the park's boundaries. There is a white pelican rookery on the islands in Lake Lavallee in the northwestern corner of the park. Double-crested cormorants are also found in the Lake Lavallee region.

The Prince Albert Park territory once was the favorite hunting and trapping grounds of Cree and Chipewyan Indians. These Indians lived in the region around Waskesiu Lake, known to them as Red Deer Lake.

One of the first white men to enter this wild region was Louis Lavallee, who built a cabin at Pelican Lake, now called Lake Lavallee in honor of him. In Lavallee's day, the region was rich with prime beavers. But, like many other species of wildlife, the beaver was trapped so frequently and wantonly that the sight of one became a rare occurrence.

Years later, another white man tried to restore the beaver in Prince Albert National Park. He was George Stanfeld Belaney, better known as "Grey Owl" (1888–1938). Belaney built a cabin on the northern edge of Ajawan Lake, and adopted Indian customs, dress, habits, and an Indian name; he also married an Iroquois maiden. All of his life Grey Owl fought for the conservation of wildlife. He wrote several books on nature, among them *Pilgrims of the Wild* (1934) and *Sajo and Her Beaver People* (1935). He became an international figure and at one time gave a talk on natural history and conservation to the king and queen of England. When not writing or lecturing, Grey Owl served as a guide and forest ranger in the region he knew and loved so well. He began his project of restoring beavers to the park in 1931, and at the time of his death in 1938, the area around Ajawan Lake was well populated with beavers once more. Grey Owl's grave and cabin are still maintained on Ajawan Lake.

Bob Smith flew around this great national park, so resplendent with wildlife, but he saw no whooping cranes. Even though this untamed region seemed to have all the natural features to support many kinds of animals and birds, the whooping cranes were not there.

While Smith was flying his waterfowl surveys and keeping an eye out for whooping cranes, the U.S. Fish and Wildlife Service dispatched two more nest hunters out on the trail. Arthur B. Hawkins and Lyle Sowls, although primarily assigned to a waterfowl survey, were asked to look for whooping cranes, too. Hawkins and Sowls drove approximately 8,000 miles by car over much of the region covered by Smith in the air. They also traveled to The Pas in northwestern Manitoba. The Pas—Canadians in that region pronounce it "Paws"—is the southern terminus of a railway that leads to Churchill on the southwestern edge of Hudson Bay. It lies in rocky terrain along the western boundary of the great Canadian Shield. There were countless lakes in the area, with plenty of waterfowl for Hawkins and Sowls to count—but no whoopers.

The summer was nearly over and the hunters had reached the end of the whooping crane trail for 1946. Pettingill, Moore, Smith, Hawkins, and Sowls had covered thousands of miles by car and plane. The total flight path was estimated at 3,750 miles, with an area of two miles on either side of the main path which had been carefully searched for signs of the cranes. When added up, the air search conducted by Pettingill, Smith, and Moore encompassed nearly 15,000 square miles of prairie, bush country, and waterways. The nest hunters had gazed down on thousands of acres of wilderness, rolling grasslands, lakes, ponds, bogs, and rivers.

While the object of their search eluded them, the hunt was not without its compensations. The Canadian Prairie Provinces were a naturalist's Mecca. Teal, canvasback, mallard, Canada goose, brant, and other waterfowl clustered on the lakes, ponds, and rivers. Loons sent their quavering calls out over the lakes to bounce against the majestic stands of conifers and ricochet around the shores in loud echoes. Hawks and eagles swung in wide circles high above the marshes and prairies. Moose, bears, wolves, raccoons, badgers, and other animals peered up as the small planes skimmed overhead. And from their observation posts in the air, the nest hunters looked down on acre after acre of dense stands of conifer and deciduous trees that carpeted the Canadian wilderness.

But no matter how interested or thrilled the nest hunters were in seeing the natural splendor of the Canadian wilderness, their thoughts always came back to one main theme: Where had the whooping cranes hidden their nesting grounds? In what remote corner, as yet undetected, did the big cranes carry on the all-important task of rearing their precious young? They had to be somewhere in all that expanse of wilderness which spanned the upper regions of the Prairie Provinces. But now, after two seasons of intensive search, the task of finding the whoopers and their nests had proved to be as difficult as locating the proverbial needle in a haystack.

Bard, Smith, Pettingill, Moore, Hawkins, and Sowls had blazed the whooper trail, but the big question was where to look the following year. The Whooping Crane Project planners had to decide whether to go back over the regions scouted in 1945 and 1946 or eliminate them from future searches.

Dr. Pettingill urged that these areas be surveyed again in 1947, and gave some good reasons for doing so. Two men flying in a small plane at 800 to 1,000 feet over open country, and at 100 to 150 feet over lakes and marshes, couldn't observe everything below them. Although they flew over specific areas, preplotted so to say, they still could see only a small fraction of the total country traversed.

Spotting birds from the air may sound like fun, but it is not easy if shy birds, such as the whooping cranes, are the objective. The combined vision range of two men in a plane, each looking to one side of the main flight path, may be likened to a four-mile aerial swath, with the plane in the center. This is a very large territory to be kept under constant observation, even by trained flyers and biologists. Cautious whooping cranes, anxious to remain inconspicuous, could easily blend into their background of marsh reeds and sedges. And variations in light conditions, encountered on gray or overcast days, constantly hamper any search from the air. This was the main reason Dr. Pettingill felt it would be wise to have future nest hunters take another look at the territories covered in the summers of 1945 and 1946.

Pettingill still believed that the whoopers were nesting somewhere north of the settlements in Saskatchewan or Alberta. He based this belief on the fact that transient whoopers had been sighted in the spring as they flew across southern Saskatchewan. After the initial sighting, the whoopers disappeared into the wilderness; Pettingill presumed that they flew on to the north. He thought the whooper nests would be found—if they ever were found —in the wild, remote northern regions of Saskatchewan or Alberta, possibly in the lake areas of these two provinces.

But all of this conjecture would have to wait until next year, if and when another search was launched. In the meantime it was obvious that more detailed information on the whoopers was needed. Nobody had ever assembled a comprehensive life history of *Grus americana,* possibly because of the scarcity of the species and an observer's inability to get within a quarter of a mile of the wary cranes. The more the biologists thought about it, the more convinced they became that perhaps a clue to the location of the nests might be found in a detailed study of the wild whoopers on the wintering-grounds.

* * *

Fall came early to the Canadian nesting grounds of the whooping cranes. Soon the cold winds would whip down from the Arctic and coat the ponds and marshes with a veneer of ice. But the cranes would not wait for icy blasts to chill them. One by one,

the big birds rose up from the nesting grounds and
pointed their heads to the south. Great wings pro-
pelled them southward with mighty flicks. And in
the middle of the valiant band of whoopers were
the three youngsters born that spring in the secret
nesting grounds.

FIVE

Bob Allen Joins the Whooper Project

When Dr. Pettingill returned to Carleton College, the Whooping Crane Project was again faced with the problem of finding a trained biologist to carry on the work so ably initiated by Bard and Pettingill. The right man appeared on the scene. Robert Porter Allen, who had been with the National Audubon Society since 1930, had just returned from four years of service with the Mine Planter Service of the U.S. Army. He resumed his duties with the Audubon Society and was assigned to the Whooping Crane Project in October, 1946.

In appointing Robert Allen to the Project, John H. Baker, President of the National Audubon Society, reported in *Audubon Magazine* that Allen would undertake a study of the life history of the whooping cranes wintering at Aransas, trace their migration route, and hunt for the breeding grounds in Canada. Eventually, Allen's study would be made into a research report. This was an ambitious program, one that demanded time, effort, and perseverance. Above all, it required an unusual person, one with patience, dedication, and professional training. Bob Allen was such a person.

Born and raised in the West Branch Valley of the Susquehanna near Williamsport, Pennsylvania, Bob Allen had a lifelong interest in wildlife. He spent most of his boyhood roaming the Bald Eagle Mountain region with his brother John, who shared his keen interest in nature, especially birds. Bob became a member of the National Audubon Society's Junior Club and corresponded with a number of prominent ornithologists while still a boy.

He attended Lafayette College in Easton, Pennsylvania, for two years, then transferred to Cornell University to study ornithology. Financial difficulties forced him to leave Cornell after three months. He became the librarian for the National Audubon Society in 1930, and by the time he entered the armed forces in 1942, Allen had built a distinguished career in the Society as librarian, sanctuary director, and research associate.

Allen was a superb naturalist and strongly dedicated to the conservation of our dwindling wildlife. He inspected bird colonies on the Atlantic and gulf coasts and made a thorough study of the rare roseate spoonbill in Florida. While pursuing the latter study, Allen moved his family down to Tavernier, a small town on the Florida Keys below Key Largo, where they all lived in a trailer.

In 1940, Bob recommended methods of saving the small surviving flock of roseate spoonbills in Florida, and his

Robert Porter Allen   *from National Audubon Society*

comprehensive report on this bird, published in 1942, was instrumental in rescuing the species from extinction. His field observations on the spoonbills were published in *Bird Lore* and *Audubon Magazine*. He also

traveled to Texas in 1941 to investigate oil pollution of
the Texas coastal waterways and marshes. His findings
were reported in *Audubon Magazine*, July–August, 1941.
Next came four years of service in the armed forces. In
1944, while still in the Army, he was elected to full
membership in the American Ornithologists' Union.

Bob Allen's impressive record with the Audubon Society made him an excellent choice to carry on the work of
the Whooping Crane Project, which he joined on a full-
time basis. In the fall of 1946, just after the whooping
cranes returned to Aransas from Canada, he launched into
his first assignment—a complete study of the birds' winter
life.

In general, the winter range of the whoopers was limited to a coastal region of approximately 10,000 acres of
salt flats, brackish ponds, and oak brush, about midway
down the Texas coast. One half of the wintering range
was within the boundaries and protection of the Aransas
Refuge. The remainder was on nearby St. Joseph and
Matagorda Islands. All of this region is transitional, lying
between the sea—represented by the Gulf of Mexico—
and the inland fresh-water areas. The dominant animal
life is marine in character, with the blue crab being an
important staple in the whooping crane diet.

The preferred wintering region for the whooping
cranes—called the east shore flats—is an area of brackish water adjacent to San Antonio Bay. The vegetation
in this region includes salt grass, saltwort, glasswort, and
salt flatgrass.

Semi-permanent ponds are scattered throughout the
flats. They are shallow, rarely more than fifty yards wide,

Whooping cranes, with other birds, in a pond on the Aransas Refuge
by John Lynch, from National Audubon Society

and their level fluctuates, depending upon the rainfall. In years when there is little rain, many of these temporary ponds dry up. The wind direction also has an important bearing on the water level. When the wind is from the east and strong, it helps to flood the ponds, and the rising waters bring with them large numbers of marine animals from the Gulf of Mexico. Waterfowl and whooping cranes quickly move in to feed on the renewed food supply.

Allen found that when there is a long drought, the water in the flats and ponds increases in salinity. This forces the cranes to seek food and drinking water in other areas, often in sections of the coast and Aransas not normally visited in an average year.

During the winter of 1946–47, Allen studied the territorial habits of the whoopers. He kept charts on the exact location of every individual pair of cranes, single birds, or family units. He learned that once the whoopers had staked out a territory, they did not leave it from late October or early November—depending upon when they returned to Aransas from Canada—until just before the spring migration.

The cranes, according to Allen's observations, actually led an isolated life, one restricted entirely to the mate or family unit. Those cranes wintering at the eastern end of the great Aransas salt flat did not come into contact with those living at the western end. However, lone cranes—either those not fully matured or those which had lost their mates—did not stake out a territory, but wandered over the sloughs and ponds at will.

Allen noticed that two sub-adult cranes would often team up and live in a territory in which there were no full-grown cranes. But these sub-adults lacked the strong attachment to a territory which was typical of a mated pair or family unit. The lone cranes rarely defended the territory, often wandering away rather than accept a challenge from another crane or family group.

Allen estimated that 400 to 500 acres of true salt flats with ponds and estuaries were required by the average pair or family of whoopers in the wintering grounds. He thought this might be an important clue to the territorial needs of the cranes in the nesting grounds.

A pair of whooping cranes near Heart Island in the whooping crane refuge, Austwell, Texas

by Allan D. Cruickshank, from National Audubon Society

At the time of Allen's field work, fourteen whooper territories were staked out in Aransas, with the average territory covering approximately 436 acres per pair of cranes or family unit. Not all of the acreage claimed by the cranes was salt flats. A portion of the territories included terrain known as oak brush. This was land about three feet higher than the sloughs and flats, and grown over with live oak, blackjack oak, and myrtleleaf oak. Below this oak brush line were the sloughs with their salt plants. All of the known whooper winter territories had frontage on one or more of the inner bays, and all contained several kinds of salt ponds found in the region.

Allen made extensive field notes on the territorial habits of the whoopers. In his opinion the general location and boundaries of whooper territories were more or less traditional. It seemed likely that the same pair of whooping cranes—and later on, their progeny—returned to the same territory year after year. There was no definite proof of this as yet, but it seemed logical to Allen.

Fully matured male whooping cranes are larger than the females. The male is the guardian of the family and territory, a fierce defender who challenges all interlopers with his loud bugle call. He is the leader of the pair or family, initiating and controlling movements from feeding place to feeding place. He remains constantly on the alert for danger, whipping his head up quickly to scan the flats, yellow eyes taking in any and all movement.

The female and the young whoopers stay close together throughout much of the winter. Most of the time the mother whooper catches food for the youngsters, breaking it up into edible bits. But she makes the young cranes pick it out of the mud near her large feet, and soon the young cranes learn to poke their bills into the mud and impale crabs or mud shrimps themselves. Once in a while the male whooper will deign to catch and prepare food for the youngsters. As a rule, though, he attends to the job of guarding and defending the family and territory.

Allen thought the intensity of the territorial defense varied in relation to the date and whether or not young cranes were present. In early spring all the whoopers more or less abandon their territories as the urge to migrate begins to work on them.

Photo by Dwight Smith, from National Audubon Society

On January 10, 1947, Allen watched two families of cranes that occupied adjacent territories. Hidden in the shelter of a live oak thicket, he saw the six cranes feeding close together in a bed of salt flatgrass. They were about a half mile away and Allen identified them as two mated pairs and two young cranes which had been brought down from Canada in the previous fall. He judged the two groups to be about twenty-five yards apart. For a while the two families fed peaceably, ignoring each other. Or so it seemed to Allen. Then the two males (identified by their more aggressive manners) detached themselves from their families and strode toward each other like two gunfighters in the old West. Allen watched the whoopers through his telescope, waiting for the males to clash.

Walking with stiff paces, their wings dragging slightly on the ground, the two male whoopers neared each other. On they marched until only a yard separated them. Then they stopped and looked around, as if sizing up the territorial boundary line, trying to decide who was infringing on whose territory. Satisfied with their quick survey, the two cranes dropped their heads down in a feeding motion. They moved closer until just two feet separated them. Again they repeated the lowering of the head in a feeding motion, then stepped backward. A minute later, they stepped toward each other. Whooper eyed whooper. Suddenly, up came their heads, bills pointing skyward, their wings drooped, and the electrifying blast of their war whoop trumpeted out over the flats. *Ker-loo! Ker-lee-oo!*

Soon the females joined in the ceremony, assuming the same posture as the beak-to-beak males. But the two youngsters remained aloof, standing off to one side. The males repeated their performance, but without any help from the females this time. After again sounding their call, the males walked away from each other, moving in small circles, head down in the customary feeding maneuver.

A few minutes later the two males came back together again, bowing their heads in short nods. Finally, they stood with their red-patched heads almost touching each other and bowed low, sending their bills into their breast feathers, almost down between their legs. All at once the ceremony was over and the two families calmly moved away, back into their respective territories.

Later, Allen reported: "The location of this demonstration had been the exact boundary between the two territorial claims!"

Gradually, Allen and Aransas biologists pieced together a comprehensive picture of the whoopers wintering at Aransas. Direct observation on territorial claims, location of the territories, defense, feeding habits, types of water areas preferred by the cranes, behavior prior to migration —all of these and more facts helped to place the whooping cranes in a better perspective.

As Allen continued his field work, he became aware of certain limiting factors governing the survival of the cranes. These limiting factors were more or less divided into two major categories: *decimating* and *welfare*. The decimating factors were those which worked against the cranes; welfare factors were those which operated in the birds' favor. Both had a very important bearing on future management of the cranes.

Unnecessary disturbance of the wintering cranes was to be avoided. So was deliberate or overmanagement of the flock. The cranes were in possession of large feeding and resting areas at Aransas, which were more than sufficient as far as the present number of cranes was concerned. The birds were able to obtain all the necessities of life within these areas. Interference with the normal behavior and environment of the cranes might prove disastrous. It was best, Allen advised, to leave them strictly alone.

The danger of cranes ranging or wandering near the intracoastal waterway was a serious potential decimating factor. Boat traffic on the waterway was increasing and whoopers might be shot by hunters in boats. Added to the waterway problem was the risk of cranes being "buzzed" or harassed by planes flying over or near the Refuge or nearby islands. The danger here lay in the possibility that the whoopers, frightened or alarmed by the planes, would desert the safety of the Refuge for other areas where they would be molested.

Another peril for the cranes was the chance that petroleum companies might come drilling for oil in the Aransas area. The discovery of oil in the marshes or waterways could be a serious blow to the welfare and conservation of the wintering whoopers. The demand for oil and its profits would quickly drown out the pleas for the safety of a mere handful of birds.

The loss of whooping cranes during migration was another major decimating factor. By studying records of cranes killed en route to and from Aransas, Allen learned that more whoopers had been killed in Nebraska than in any other state along the migration trail. This deplorable fact pointed up the need to establish a refuge or resting station along the Platte River in the vicinity visited by the cranes on their flights north or south.

Allen realized that certain characteristics of the whoopers acted as decimating factors. Unfortunately, they could not be controlled by management. These self-decimating factors included the fact that the species was migratory, and required vast tracts of specialized wilderness for breeding purposes. Just how long such wilderness would be available was an unknown factor. Also, the big cranes were noisy birds who drew attention to themselves, and thus became easy targets for hunters or destructionists. Whooping cranes were monogamous; they mated for life and did not take a new mate if they lost their first. This was a factor which could work against them insofar as reproducing the species was concerned. Whoopers were also fiercely loyal birds and would remain near a dead or wounded mate, thus placing themselves in danger.

Allen believed that the whoopers did not breed until they were several years old. And past records attested to the fact that when they did, only two eggs were laid. Allen also reasoned that, like the offspring of sandhill cranes, young whoopers could not fly until they were several months old. Their inability to fly would expose them to predators. No losses from predators had been recorded at Aransas, but this might be a major decimating factor in the breeding grounds.

Other factors that could decimate the crane population were fires, drought, lowering of water tables, and drainage of marshes. Disease was another important consideration. While not much was known about whooping crane diseases, data on sandhill crane diseases were available. Dr. Lawrence H. Walkinshaw, a leading authority on the sandhill cranes, reported that sandhills died from limberneck (botulism), tuberculosis, and fowl cholera. It was possible that the whoopers were also subject to these diseases.

Cattle were permitted to graze in certain areas of Aransas, and Allen was concerned about the unfavorable effect this practice might have on the whoopers. Therefore, he made a special study of this factor in the winter of 1946–47. Two areas were staked out in two more or less similar sections of salt flat and oak brush. One of these areas was enclosed with a cattle-proof fence; the other was left unfenced. The fenced area contained a combined salt flat and oak brush territory of approximately one square mile. Since no cattle were permitted in this enclosure, it remained free from grazing, trampling, and other cattle marks. The unfenced area was turned over to the cattle.

Later, upon comparing the two areas, it was apparent that no serious or lasting damage to the cranes was caused by cattle. The cows did trample on crab burrows, shrimp holes, and Neredi worm tunnels, but the damage was not extensive. Plants were damaged, of course, but these were plants not utilized by whoopers. Allen's conclusion was that while cattle did no extensive damage to the whooping crane habitat, it was best to keep them out of the whooper territories.

On the plus or welfare factor side, the cranes themselves provided some safeguards. Even though they were noisy birds, their shyness prevented them from being caught. They were quite able to defend themselves and their young against most predators. Also, there was the possibility that whooping cranes had a long lifespan. Finally, better state and federal protection could help save the whoopers. While they already had some protection, a way had not yet been found to prevent hunters from shooting them down along the migration route.

Allen was aware that the public's interest in the plight of the whooping cranes had steadily increased, thanks to the excellent publicity begun by Charles Broley, Fred Bard, and others connected with the Whooping Crane Project. Even persons in regions remote from the whoopers had voiced concern over the desperate situation facing the big cranes.

But the male population of small towns and farms along the migration route was still taking to the field with guns. Allen advocated the immediate launching of a strong and intensive educational program, geared to reach these men and boys. With the whooping cranes at such a dangerously low point in numbers, the death of even a single one at the hands of a hunter would be a calamity. And a mass attack on the whoopers—a wholesale slaughter like that once performed on the hawks and falcons soaring down the Kittatinny Mountain range in eastern Pennsylvania before the Hawk Mountain Sanctuary came into being— would be likely to end the program and the species forever.

Allen recommended that articles and features on whooping cranes should be placed in hunting magazines, conservation department periodicals, and farm journals. He urged that school children be told about the whooping cranes; an educational program aimed at children could be a major and fertile area of conservation, if properly exploited. He suggested that information on the whoopers be sent to Junior Audubon Clubs, Boy and Girl Scout troops, 4-H Clubs, and Future Farmers of America groups in the migration states.

Allen stressed the enlistment of youth time and time again. He stated: "If we fail and the last whooping crane is shot by an unidentified man or boy out for a little 'sport,' we can be sure of one thing: that man or boy was never an active member of a Junior Audubon Club. The present challenge is to reach this individual, and to reach him now. His hand will be raised to salute or destroy. What shall it be?"

Finally, Allen thought that the nesting grounds, when located, should be set aside as a refuge. And, if needed, a study and management of the grounds should be initiated as soon as possible after their discovery.

SIX

The Hunt Continues—1947

All during the winter of 1946–47, the whooping cranes roamed through the Aransas sloughs and ponds, skillfully probing in the brackish water and thick mud for tasty marine animals. When the cranes weren't hunting for food, they moved up into the oak brush and preened themselves. Occasionally, there were territorial disputes and squabbles when a family or lone crane trespassed on the domain of another family or group. Bob Allen and the Aransas biologists, hidden in the oak brush or behind a canvas blind, watched the whoopers day after day, constantly adding more and more data to the slowly emerging life history of the whooping cranes.

March came and with it arrived the promise of spring. The whoopers now shifted their territories, moving from the sloughs and ponds up to higher ground. It was the time of pre-migration urges when the cranes forsook their strict territorial boundaries and wandered almost at will, even into the backyards of other whooper families or pairs. They did more flying now, climbing above the sloughs and swinging through the sky in large circles. And down on the ground, when the March winds shook their feathers, the cranes shuffled into the strange prenuptial dance. Soon the migration urge would be too strong to resist and they would again fly off to the northwest, leaving Aransas and its puzzled scientists behind them.

The urge to migrate was just as mysterious as the destination of the big cranes. What makes birds migrate, cranes as well as other species? Some ornithologists believe that migration is part of a cycle in which reproduction plays a prominent role. The two are very closely related, for cranes and other migratory birds return to their breeding grounds to nest, and depart as soon as the young are able to fly and fend for themselves. Biologists have long sought a cause-and-effect relationship between bird migration and reproduction.

Other ornithologists think that the spring migration is prompted by a renewed activity of the birds' gonadal glands. Perhaps this gonadal renewal is stimulated by the lengthening of the days in spring—by what scientists might call variations in photo-periodism. Fall migration then would be triggered by an opposite reaction, a regression of the gonadal activity. Ornithologists who hold to this theory also believe that the increase or decrease in temperatures plays a major part in the migration impulse.

There is another theory which states that many birds are descended from ancestors that once lived in the northern zones before the glaciers. When the great glaciers slithered southward, these prehistoric birds were forced to move south, ahead of the creeping seas of ice. But some instinctive memory causes them to fly back to the north again. Yet another theory takes an opposite view: that most birds are of southern zone origin and fly north in the spring simply because of crowded territories and keen competition for food.

Whatever the reasons for migrations, countless numbers of birds rise up each year from their wintering grounds and fly with unerring navigation to northern breeding grounds.

While the whooping cranes were preparing for the spring migration, Bob Allen set out in late March for the Platte River in Nebraska. It was believed that the whoopers flew a direct route from Aransas north through west-central Oklahoma and Kansas, and on to Nebraska where they stopped somewhere on the Platte River. Allen's job was to find just where the whoopers came down on the Platte. He was to check all reports on the cranes and sight the birds, if possible. Olaf Wallmo, assistant to the Aransas biologists, was assigned the task of charting the departure of the whoopers from Aransas and relaying this information to Allen.

Allen took his wife and children along in a caravan consisting of a station wagon, car, and trailer. As the family drove up through Oklahoma, they found many people interested in the whooping cranes. *Life Magazine* had run a feature on the whoopers, including some excellent photographs taken by Andreas Feininger at Aransas. Thanks to this feature and to the public relations work of Seth

Low, biologist at the Salt Plains Refuge near Jet, Oklahoma, more and more Oklahomans had become whooper conscious. The same was true in Kansas, where U.S. Game Management Agent Melvin Ramsey and State Game Protector Arthur Jones had "talked up" the whooper at every opportunity. This increased interest in the whooping cranes was encouraging news to Allen and others participating in the Whooping Crane Project. The rare cranes could never have enough friends, especially along the dangerous migration route.

The Allen family was met in North Platte, Nebraska, by a delegation of the Sportsmen's Association from Lincoln County. In the delegation was Wilson Trout, editor of the local newspaper, a weekly, and author of *Lincoln County Birds*. Trout escorted the Allens to the Hotel Pawnee, their home for the next five weeks.

The north and south tributaries of the Platte River meet at North Platte, and from there the river flows eastward, curving broadly at Plattsmouth and rolling on into the wide Missouri. The Platte is a fairly wide but shallow river with a large portion of its course shunted here and there by sand bars. These sand bars break the river up into many channels. In dry periods, the river shrinks to a mere stream, but in the spring it becomes a torrential waterway fed by the melting snows of the Rocky Mountains.

Broad and fertile, the Platte River valley runs through the entire center of Nebraska. The state itself is a vast region of immense prairies which rise gradually toward the Rockies in the west. This great prairie once was hunted over by Omaha, Pawnee, Otoe, and Dakotah Indians. The North Platte River formed part of the celebrated Oregon Trail over which stolid oxen hauled bouncing Conestoga wagons, while weary pioneers, their faces tanned or reddened by the blistering sun, trudged alongside. But if the emigrants sighted whooping cranes, we'll never know, for few of them kept journals or diaries. Their energies went into keeping the wagons moving and hostile Indians away.

The North Platte Bird Club volunteered to help Allen look for cranes along the Platte. This suited Allen; the more eyes searching for the whoopers, the better it would be. Nebraskans, from Ogallala on the western boundary of the state to Grand Island in the east, were alerted for whoopers. The *North Platte Telegraph Bulletin* carried a long article on Allen and the whooping cranes. Readers were told what a whooper looked like and which birds might be mistaken for whooping cranes (pelican, egret, snow goose, sandhill crane, etc.). The readers were also advised to communicate with Allen if they saw—or thought they saw—whooping cranes.

As a result of this article, Allen was deluged with telephone calls, telegrams, letters, and personal visits from farmers, teachers, school children, pilots, and various other persons, all of whom claimed to have sighted whooping cranes. Allen thanked them and checked out their reports. Regrettably, all the sightings proved to be white pelicans, snow geese, and sandhill cranes. But the important point was that people were interested enough in the whoopers to look for them. And more people, listening to broadcasts about the whoopers from radio station KODY, found themselves staring at every large bird, secretly hoping that they would be the first ones to sight the big cranes.

Allen was waiting on the Platte for the whoopers when Olaf Wallmo wired the news that a total of twenty-three had departed from Aransas between April 6th and 18th. If the cranes followed past patterns, they should be arriving at the Platte very soon. April was still a cold month, but Allen maintained a daily lookout for the migrating whoopers. He sighted many snow geese, white pelicans, and sandhill cranes, but as yet there was no sign of the whooping cranes.

Then Allen received a telephone call from State Conservation Officer Lee Jensen, who was stationed at North Platte. Jensen advised Allen to go out to Earl Mather's farm right away. Mather had reported seeing five whooping cranes! Allen leaped into his car and raced out to the farm. Mather said he and his wife had seen the whoopers in a pasture, but when Allen searched the area, he saw nothing but some white pelicans.

Thanking Mather for his cooperation, Allen courteously explained that the birds were white pelicans, not whooping cranes. Mather shook his head stubbornly; the pelicans weren't the birds he meant. He knew what a pelican was! The birds he and Mrs. Mather had seen in the pasture were whooping cranes and they went "thataway"; the farmer pointed toward the South Platte.

Allen didn't stay to argue. He drove immediately to the local airport, chartered a plane, and flew over to the Platte. Within ten minutes after taking off, Allen and the pilot sighted five whooping cranes standing on a sand bar in the South Platte due south of the airport. Allen recognized an immature crane among them as one belonging to what the Aransas biologists called the "North Group." The youngster was accompanied by its parents. Wallmo had reported that this particular group left Aransas on April 13th, and Allen sighted them on April 19th. Therefore he could say conclusively that it took the birds six days to fly from Aransas to the Platte River.

After resting and feeding, the five cranes rose up from the sand bar and flew toward the north. Past observations had shown that the whoopers traveled in a more or less straight line from Aransas to Saskatchewan, a distance of approximately 1,600 miles. Since the whoopers probably made several other stops to feed and rest besides the one on the Platte, they undoubtedly added a few hundred miles to the trip.

Allen and his family remained in North Platte until April 27th, when they set out in their caravan for Regina. They arrived there on May 1st, and shortly afterwards Allen met with Fred Bard at the Provincial Museum of Natural History. Reports on the whoopers were coming in and a definite flight pattern was beginning to develop. The cranes appeared to fan out after they reached the short grass prairie and aspen parkland zones. These areas extended from the U.S.–Manitoba boundary northwest across southern Saskatchewan. This is a great wheat-producing region, and it had once been the site of a whooper nest—the one discovered at Muddy Lake, Saskatchewan, in 1922. Bard thought this region was the one that should be explored first. If it turned out to be unproductive, then the search could be moved northward and westward.

Two more whooping crane hunters, Dr. Lawrence H. Walkinshaw and Walter Tholen, both of Battle Creek, Michigan, arrived in Regina in May. Dr. Walkinshaw, a dentist, had an impressive background as a naturalist and ornithologist. His specialty was the sandhill cranes. Walkinshaw's interest in sandhill cranes dated to 1930, when he had found several sandhills in one of the large marshes in Calhoun County, Michigan. At that time the sandhill cranes were not too plentiful and their future appeared dim. Walkinshaw was appointed the head of a committee concerned with saving the birds, and a major step was taken to protect them when 571 acres of marsh were bought from a farmer in Calhoun County and another marsh obtained in Jackson County.

In 1939, the Cranbrook Institute of Science asked Dr. Walkinshaw to write a monograph on the life history of the sandhill cranes. He was at work on this project when John H. Baker, President of the National Audubon Society, asked him to help find the whooper nests. Walkinshaw had headed an expedition to central Alberta some years before in search of sandhill cranes and therefore was familiar with the general nature of the terrain. He agreed to hunt for the whoopers during his vacation and asked a close friend, Walter Tholen, to accompany him. Tholen was not an ornithologist—his profession was accounting —but he had a strong interest in wildlife and in saving the whooping crane. Both he and Walkinshaw were traveling at their own expense.

Fred Bard still thought that the most promising areas for whoopers were in a region in west-central Saskatchewan and eastern Alberta. This region started at the

Beaver River and extended north to the Clearwater. Another promising area, according to Bard's reports, began north of Nipawin, extending from Montreal Lake, east of Prince Albert National Park, to Flin Flon and The Pas in Manitoba. These areas had been scouted unsuccessfully by Pettingill, Moore, and Smith in the summer of 1946. However, Bard thought they were worth another search because of sighting and migration trend reports he had received in 1946 and 1947. Walkinshaw and Tholen were asked to explore the Nipawin area, while Allen covered the Beaver River region.

In checking the reports on whooper flights, Allen perceived that the main flight path in Canada seemed to head a little to the west of north in the direction of the Beaver River. It passed over settlements, such as Loon Lake, Goodsoil, Makwa, and Meadow Lake, and then the trail was lost. Allen thought the cranes might be heading up to Lake Claire in Alberta or to the wilderness beyond, but this was only a guess on his part. He agreed with Bard that it would be wise to check out the two Saskatchewan regions before carrying the search west and north. He also hoped that he could make a search beyond Clearwater, perhaps going as far north as Great Slave Lake in the District of Mackenzie, Northwest Territories. Pettingill had recommended this area after his fruitless hunt the previous summer.

Once again the nomadic Allen family started off in their caravan. This time they drove to Meadow Lake on the edge of the Canadian bush country, where they arrived on May 11th. Meadow Lake, located on the shore of the lake of the same name, was a frontierish town with clapboard buildings and very primitive accommodations. But the Allens were rugged pioneers and soon adapted to the hardships of the bush country. Bob met with Jim Barnett, the District Game Superintendent, and both men examined maps of the proposed search areas. Meanwhile, Mrs. Barnett, a schoolteacher, went over lessons with the Allen children, who were being tutored in whatever places the whooper search took them.

Allen decided to set up a base camp on Flotten Lake about forty-five miles north of Meadow Lake in Meadow Lake Provincial Park. He and the family moved there a few days later. Flotten Lake was the northern terminus of the paved roads in that mixed woodland region of the Boreal Forest, and it was within the search area which Bard considered likely to contain whooping cranes.

Even though it was the middle of May, Flotten Lake was coated with ice. The weather was stormy and chill winds, accompanied by rain and hail, shook the Allen tent from morning to night. The nights were cold, with the temperature dropping to 32 degrees F., but very short because there were only four hours of darkness at that latitude.

When the cold eased and the ice broke up a few days later, Allen was able to move freely around the area. He saw many birds, including loons and grebes, but no whooping cranes. Several old-timers told him they remembered seeing whoopers years before, and he asked forest rangers, bush pilots, hunters and trappers, all of whom knew the region well, if they had any ideas about potential nesting sites. Unfortunately, no one could suggest any likely places in the immediate vicinity, so Allen then questioned them about the character of the country farther north and west, the region near Fort McMurray and Lake Claire.

By the end of May, Allen had formulated his search plans. Bob Smith was to bring the search plane to Flotten Lake around June 1st, and Allen arranged for the delivery of 1,000 gallons of gasoline, which would be stored at the base camp. Smith was five days late when he flew to Flotten Lake from Prince Albert on June 6th. Two days later, he and Allen took off to search the wilderness from Flotten Lake north and westward to Great Slave Lake in Alberta.

* * *

The whoopers had been housekeeping on their secret nesting grounds since the end of April. They had built strong, large nests, well hidden from predators. Each nest was woven out of rushes and grass and had a diameter of three feet. The nests were placed in the shallow end of the pond where the water was only eighteen inches deep. The tops of the nests rose to about fifteen inches above the surface of the surrounding water. All of the nests were in the middle of thick vegetation. Several trails led from them into the sedges and cattails, where the whoopers rested and preened themselves when the midday sun burned too hotly on the open waters.

In a large nest that seemed to float on the water, a female crane sat incubating two eggs. The eggs were long and narrow and olive-buff in color. They

blended well into the background of nesting material, a natural camouflage that made the eggs almost invisible from the sky or pond.

Now it was the male whooper's turn to incubate the eggs. The female carefully raised herself on the nest, moving slowly so as not to bump or step on the eggs. She stood up, jumped off the nest, raised her wings and flapped them several times, then strolled away into the pond.

Stepping gingerly onto the nest, the male arranged his legs on either side of the eggs and sank down to a reversed kneeling position, with foreshanks bent in front. He eyed the eggs and then slowly and lightly settled down on top of them.

A few minutes later the female sounded an alarm and darted quickly into the sedges to the left of the nest. The male stiffened and sat absolutely still. Holding her wings aloft, the female jabbed her powerful bill again and again at something in the sedges, close to the water's edge. A startled beaver made a hasty retreat from the nest, plunging into the water with the irate female striding after him, her wings waggling in anger. The beaver reached deep water and quickly disappeared under the surface. He came to the top far from the crane, looked back at the scolding whooper, and then swam toward the far end of the pond. Still bristling with anger, the female strode back to the nest, where the male broke out of his statue-like pose.

Soon all was serene again around the whooper nest
and the cranes took turns incubating the eggs.
While one crane kept the eggs warm and turned
them, the other kept guard. Nothing, not even so
much as a frog, was permitted near the nest and the
precious eggs. Before long, if all went well, the
nesting site would vibrate with the shrill peeps of
newborn whooper chicks.

*   *   *

Dr. Walkinshaw and Walter Tholen left Fred Bard in
Regina and proceeded to Yorkton in Saskatchewan, close
to the Manitoba border. Walkinshaw hired pilot Austin
Ingham to fly them over the Nipawin region. Before they
left the Yorkton area they scouted the area around Saltcoats, including Saltcoats District Regional Park and
nearby Rockeby Marsh. There were no whoopers in these
regions and Walkinshaw had the pilot fly them west to
Last Mountain Lake. After covering this lake and finding
no whoopers, Walkinshaw, Tholen, and Ingham flew
northeast to Little Quill and Big Quill lakes, about 125
miles south of Nipawin. They found no whoopers on either of these two lakes and flew on up to Nipawin on the
north branch of the Saskatchewan River.

Nipawin, at that time only a few years old, was on the
edge of the extensive coniferous region of central Canada.
Beyond and north of the town stretched a vast expanse of
jack pine, spruce, and muskeg. When he had hunted
sandhill cranes in Alberta, Walkinshaw had found that
these birds nested in boggy muskeg, as well as marshes.
Therefore, he decided to search the muskegs north of
Nipawin for whooping cranes. He and Tholen flew as

much as four hours at a time over the muskegs, usually about 300 to 400 feet above the bogs. When they wanted a broader view, they flew higher. But their careful search of the area north of Nipawin failed to produce a single whooping crane.

Walkinshaw and Tholen then traveled to Prince Albert, where they met up with Bob Allen and Bob Smith, who were about to head north and west. Flying with some Canadians over the region north of Prince Albert, Walkinshaw and Tholen saw some white pelicans, but no other large birds. Late in June, their vacation over, the two men returned to Michigan. Meanwhile, Allen and Smith were covering every likely pond, lake, and marsh south of the Clearwater River. Having sighted no whooping cranes in this region, they pointed their plane toward the next block of terrain to be searched. This was the territory around Lake Claire, north of Fort McMurray and west of Lake Athabaska in Alberta. Pettingill and Moore had made a circuit around Lake Claire in 1946, and Pettingill and his wife, Eleanor, had camped in the great marsh east of Lake Claire near Fort Chipewyan.

Pettingill had recommended to the Project that this region be searched again, for the marshes around Lake Claire provided excellent waterfowl habitat, even though they were subject to inroads by Chipewyan Indians. While there were no reports of Indians finding whooping cranes or molesting them, there was a possibility that the region was too public for a whooping crane nesting site. Still, Allen and Smith made a thorough search of the marshes and Lake Claire itself.

Finding no whoopers in the Lake Claire region, Allen and Smith flew farther north to Great Slave Lake in the District of Mackenzie. The nest hunters were now in the huge Northwest Territories region of Canada. Great Slave Lake was discovered by Samuel Hearne in 1771, but was not completely explored until 1921. It has an area of 11,170 square miles, with a length of 300 miles and a width of 30 to 140 miles. This huge lake is fed by the Yellowknife, Slave, and Hay rivers and various small tributaries, and is drained by the Mackenzie River, which flows north to the Arctic Ocean. Gold was discovered on the north shore of Great Slave Lake in 1934 and prospectors flocked to the region.

On the north shore of the lake is Yellowknife, a major mining center in the Northwest Territories. Uranium is its newest boom. Yellowknife is the headquarters of the Giant Yellowknife Mines, the fourth largest uranium mine in Canada. While Allen and Smith were hunting the whooping cranes and their nests, mining engineers were prowling through the region searching for the yellow stains of uranium oxide and the blue-gray ore that sends the geiger counters jumping back and forth.

Canadian Government geologists were also exploring the shores of Yellowknife Bay on Great Slave Lake. They reported favorably to the government and recommended that 3,000 square miles should be prospected for uranium. The results of this report were a new mining boom and a fresh stampede of prospectors into Yellowknife.

But while the mining experts were meeting with success, the whooping crane nest hunters were experiencing failure. Allen and Smith found no whoopers on Great

Slave Lake or in the surrounding region, and on June 23rd, they flew back to Fort Smith on the northeastern boundary of Alberta. Fort Smith boasted an airstrip, a small hotel, and about 1,000 inhabitants, and the two biologists decided to use the town as a new base of operations.

Fort Smith is on the Slave River north of Fort Fitzgerald in the District of Mackenzie. The Slave River Delta is broad and flat and the marshes stretch for miles, providing a home for thousands of ducks, geese, gulls, and pelicans. Eagles and hawks soar over the marshes and ravens croak hoarsely as they squabble over food. Moose and black bears roam the region, and there are millions of black flies—the scourge of both men and animals.

Operating from Fort Smith, Allen and Smith flew over the Salt River west of the settlement as far as the Grand Detour, which is located between the Slave and Little Buffalo rivers. The Grand Detour is an immense grassy plain extending as far as the eye can see, rising up at the horizon to meet the sky. It is wild, desolate country, but it seemed to be shunned by the whoopers.

Smith next guided the plane to the parklands near the Tethul and Taltson rivers, east of the Slave. He and Allen cruised slowly over these parklands, but saw no whoopers. Swinging west, they flew across the delta of the Slave and on over to Fort Resolution and Pine Point on the south shore of Great Slave Lake. From here, they headed southwest to the Hay River. Still no signs of whooping cranes!

Time was getting short, for June 25th was to be the last day of the hunt. On that day Allen and Smith flew up the

Hay River as far as Big Island at the head of the great
Mackenzie River. From Big Island they traveled along the
north shore of Great Slave Lake around to Deep Bay and
Slave Point. The north arm of Deep Bay was still en-
crusted with pockets of ice. Beyond all this region was
timberland, interspersed with scattered muskeg, which
did not appear at all promising as a whooping crane nesting site.

Just north of the 60th parallel, Smith pivoted the plane
around and flew back to Great Slave Lake, scouting its
southern border and also nearby Buffalo Lake. Seeing no
cranes anywhere, Smith and Allen headed back toward
Fort Smith. Their course carried them over the northern
portion of Wood Buffalo Park, a region of tamarack-
muskeg marked with large potholes. After crossing the
upper reaches of the Klewi and Sass rivers, they ran into a
severe rainstorm. Although visibility was near zero, and
high winds were buffeting the light plane, Smith managed
to nurse it along, and they finally touched down on the
airstrip at Fort Smith at 2:45 P.M. This ended the hunt for
1948, since Allen had no more search areas on his list for
that year.

Allen and Smith had flown a total of fifteen flight days,
from June 6th to the 25th, and had covered 5,760 miles.
Altogether, considering the observation path on either
side of the plane, the two biologists had scouted more
than 23,000 square miles of Canadian wilderness without
seeing a single whooping crane. The cranes had to be
somewhere in that seemingly endless land of lakes, rivers,
ponds, and muskegs. But where?

*   *   *

The first frost glazed the surface of the Canadian ponds and marshes when the last family of whoopers rose up to the sky with quick wingbeats. They pointed their heads to the south and once again began the long trip to Aransas. Later that fall, the big cranes landed on the sloughs at Aransas with six youngsters born that spring in the still secret nesting grounds.

SEVEN

The Far North—1948

After three extensive searches, the location of the whooping crane breeding grounds was just as much of a mystery as ever. Those who had warned the nest hunters that the search would be a difficult one had known what they were talking about. Bard, Smith, Pettingill, Moore, and now Allen and Walkinshaw had scouted an enormous portion of the Canadian wilderness without seeing a single whooping crane.

The failure to even sight a whooper was difficult to understand, since the cranes were observed entering Saskatchewan; many reports by amateur and experienced observers attested to this fact. The cranes didn't leave the continent; at least no reports of whoopers sighted anywhere else in the world had been received by the Whooping Crane Project personnel. How could a handful of whooping cranes disappear so completely?

The search for the nesting grounds had attracted considerable attention in the United States, Canada, and even as far away as the British Isles. Magazines and newspapers, quick to scent feature story material, gave the whooping cranes liberal space and coverage. Sometimes these publicity stories helped the cause; other times they hindered it or created complications.

One national magazine advised its readers to report any sighting of a huge white bird to a federal, state, or local conservation official. No mention was made of the fact that the whooping cranes traveled up and down a relatively narrow flyway from Texas to Saskatchewan, and for many months after the article appeared in 1947, Allen and other conservationists were bombarded with reports of "huge white birds" sighted all over the United States and Canada. While most of these reports were valueless because of the location, conservationists were glad that so many people were becoming aware of the great cranes and their fight for survival.

On the other hand, while Allen and other Whooping Crane Project participants were winning friends for the cranes, a number of skeptics and scoffers appeared on the scene. A leading Canadian magazine mentioned that in 1948, some of North America's eminent wildlife experts would be searching more than 250,000 square miles of muskegs in northwestern Canada for whooper nests. The hunt, according to this magazine, had already cost $75,-000 and the nest hunters didn't have even one egg to show for it.

Actually, the searches for the breeding grounds were being conducted on a very low budget. One of the biggest cost factors was the chartering of planes to fly over the search areas, and the hunters had tried various ways of getting around this. Fred Bard, in the summer of 1945, had attempted to hitchhike rides on U.S. Air Force planes, but managed only the one trip from Watson Lake to Dease Lake. Terris Moore flew his own plane on the 1946 expedition, and Walkinshaw and Tholen hunted the nests at their own expense in 1947. True, Bob Smith and other U.S. Fish and Wildlife Service personnel did look for whooping cranes. But they were obliged to make waterfowl surveys in the search areas anyway, and including one more bird in the survey was no hardship on the taxpayers. Allen and Smith were also on waterfowl surveys in the summer of 1947, and what searching they did for whooping cranes was no obstacle to their other duties. Finally, Allen's food, lodging, and travel expenses to and from Canada were paid for by the National Audubon Society.

"The total amount of each taxpayer's direct contribution to our search," commented Allen in his research report on the northern breeding grounds (1952), "wouldn't cover the cost of a penny postcard to their congressmen. Which is too bad, for some sharing of the burden might have hastened a feeling of public concern and responsibility and greatly increased public interest in such problems."

However, there were many who supported the searches, and from them Allen and other conservationists obtained renewed inspiration and determination for another search in 1948. But again, a national magazine—unwittingly, or perhaps because of poor journalistic methods—confused the issue.

This magazine devoted three pages of photographs to

the whooping cranes. There was nothing wrong with the photographs; they were excellent shots of the cranes on the wintering grounds in Aransas. But one caption stated that conservationists planned to trail the whoopers to their nesting grounds by plane. This statement caused no end of trouble, giving readers the impression that Allen would actually follow the cranes day and night on their migration, keeping his plane on their tails, so to say.

Letters, wires, and telephone calls, for and against the idea, came in for a long time afterwards, and Allen and others were kept busy explaining that they planned no such maneuver for the next or any future searches. First of all, the idea was impractical. Whooping cranes averaged forty to forty-five miles an hour, and it would be virtually impossible to throttle a plane down to that speed. Secondly, the cranes didn't like planes and there was no telling what they would do if one came close to them. After much patient explanation, the furor caused by this erroneous report finally quieted down.

All sorts of other suggestions were made to the Project leaders, but these proved equally impractical. One advised the use of "radar bands" or "radio active bands" —presumably attached to the cranes—as a way of tracking the whoopers to their nesting grounds. Something of this kind has been done in the case of grizzly bears. The huge bears have been tranquilized, then fitted with a tracking device so that their wanderings and hibernations could be studied by scientists. But a similar technique was out of the question for the whoopers, since no one was able to suggest how the cranes could be caught and banded without injury. The big birds were extremely difficult to capture and usually put up a fierce struggle for freedom. There were far too few cranes to risk injury or death with such a method.

As Allen and the others shaped the plans for the 1948 search, they were governed both by the failures of the three previous hunts and by some new information that came in between August, 1947, and April, 1948. This information indicated that there was a definite trend in the flight of the whoopers after they passed over into Saskatchewan. The flyway of waterfowl seemed to channel northward beyond the Clearwater River, and follow the Athabaska, Slave, and Mackenzie River routes. This was a natural migration path of ducks, geese, and swans, and it could very well be the route taken by the whoopers also.

Since both Manitoba and Saskatchewan had been thoroughly checked without finding any traces of whooping cranes, it was felt that these two provinces could safely be taken off the search list. Most of the likely whooper nesting sites in Alberta had been covered, too. Allen and Smith had examined the great marshes and prairies around Lake Claire and the delta regions of the Athabaska, Birch, and Peace rivers without observing any cranes. They had also inspected the salt plains and aspen parklands along the Slave, Tethul, and Taltson rivers with the same negative results.

There was only one large region likely to contain whooping cranes that had not been searched: the far north, that seemingly endless wilderness in the District of Mackenzie, including the Mackenzie River basin, the Mackenzie Delta on the Arctic Sea, the Kugaluk and

The Canadian Far North

Anderson rivers, and the broad stretch of land reaching northwest to Alaska.

A careful examination of maps of this proposed northern search area showed Allen that there were regions which could provide excellent waterfowl habitats. If this was true, the possibility of whooping cranes being in these regions was good. Allen and the others who were planning the 1948 search decided to extend the hunt north of the 60th parallel, into the wilderness of the Northwest Territories.

The District of Mackenzie, Northwest Territories, is a huge, lonely expanse of land embracing 527,490 square miles, including 34,265 square miles of fresh-water surface. Much of the region is undeveloped and remote, and many areas have never been explored. The District is situated between the Yukon Territory on the west and the District of Keewatin on the east. Its physiographic regions, from west to east, are the Mackenzie Mountains (part of the Cordillera), the Mackenzie lowlands of the Interior Plains, and a portion of the Canadian Shield.

The District of Mackenzie is north of the deciduous tree line of North America. Most of the Mackenzie River basin has a landscape known as taiga, or northern coniferous forests, composed of black and white spruce, fir, jack pine and tamarack, interspersed with thickets of alder, birch, and juniper. The thickness of the growth depends on the soil and drainage. When the taiga is burned over or cleared and then allowed to grow again, aspens and birches appear first, but are eventually replaced by conifers.

North of the taiga in the Arctic section of the District is the tundra, or Arctic barrens. Here the vegetation consists of grasses, sedges, mosses, flowering herbs, dwarf willows, and birches. There are vast regions of permafrost, perennially frozen ground below the depths usually reached by seasonal thaws. This permafrost may range from a few inches to several feet; it extends down 1,000 feet in parts of Alaska and 2,000 feet in sections of Siberia! Distinctive features of this terrain are thaw lakes and sinkholes.

The Mackenzie River system, the twelfth longest river system in the world, is navigable from the 60th parallel. Its chief tributaries are the Liard, South Nahanni, Great Bear, Peel, Athabaska, and Slave rivers. The South Nahanni River has some of the most spectacular mountain and canyon scenery in the world, including the Virginia Falls which are 316 feet high. East of the Mackenzie basin is the Coppermine River which drains the Canadian Shield portion of the District north into the Arctic Sea.

Beginning at Great Slave Lake, the Mackenzie flows northwest and is fed along the way by its various tributaries. The Liard roars down from the Yukon, tumbling in fierce rapids to empty into the Mackenzie at Fort Simpson. It originates at Dease Lake in British Columbia, the lake to which Fred Bard made his useless flight in 1945 on the first search for the whooper nests.

Farther down its course, the Mackenzie is joined by the Great Bear River which drains Great Bear Lake. Great Bear Lake is an inland sea, the largest North American lake with the exception of Superior, Huron, and Michigan. This remote lake is almost always frozen until the last week in July.

The Hudson's Bay Company kept posts in the Great

Bear Lake region for more than 100 years, and one of its employees, Gilbert Labine, discovered a great silver lode on the lake's shore. But the discovery brought Labine little wealth, since the cost of transporting the silver from Great Bear Lake proved to be far more than the silver was worth. Labine also discovered pitchblende on the lake, the substance first used to refine radium. And out of the pitchblende mine at Great Bear Lake came the uranium that was used to fission the atomic bombs dropped on Japan in 1945.

Flanked by the Mackenzie Mountains on the west and the Franklin Mountains on the east, the Mackenzie basin is a region of taiga and marsh. Wildlife is abundant. There are countless ducks, geese, and pelicans in the marshes. Moose, mule deer, wood buffalo, black bears, and snowshoe rabbits roam the forests. Important fur-bearing animals in the river basin are the muskrat, beaver, mink, and marten. Hawks and eagles wheel in the skies overhead. Many other birds summer in this region, among them the familiar robin, yellow warbler, ruffed grouse, and Canada jay.

One of the first white men to explore this great basin was Alexander Mackenzie, the young Scot fur trader of the Northwest Company. He and a small party left Fort Chipewyan on June 3, 1789, and paddled down the Slave River in birchbark canoes. Swift rapids forced them to portage six times on the Slave, and they had to fight off continually the swarms of black flies that covered a man's face in a twinkling. Mackenzie, in addition to locating fur trapping sites, sought the Northwest Passage, the supposed short cut to the Orient.

Twenty-three days later, Mackenzie arrived at Great Slave Lake. After briefly exploring the region, the party continued on down the river that now bears Mackenzie's name. The frail canoes shot rapids which ran faster than twelve knots. The most spectacular section of the river was below Norman Wells, where the water coursed smoothly through high limestone cliffs that lined both sides of the river, forming a canyon seven miles long. At times, the river was 200 feet deep. Mackenzie and his party finally reached the delta on the Arctic Ocean on July 12, 1789, completing a remarkable journey for those times.

Just before the Mackenzie River empties into the Arctic Ocean, it splits up into many channels which form a patchwork of water and muskeg stretching over a 1,500-mile area. This is the great Mackenzie Delta, a huge water-and-land region that provides excellent habitats for thousands of birds. Allen and other biologists wondered if this waterway might contain the whoopers.

While the 1948 search was still in the planning stage, several reports came into the Whooper Project headquarters. These recommended specific regions in which to search for the cranes. A consulting geologist in Vancouver, British Columbia, suggested that the 1948 search include the wilderness contained within the boundaries of the lower Peace River to the south, the Slave River on the east, Great Slave Lake to the north, and the Hay River on the west. The geologist said he knew this region very well and that it was an ideal habitat for whooping cranes. It was away from the crowds of hunters, and contained plenty of marshes, sloughs, and open prairie lands, as well as an abundant food supply for waterfowl. Allen and Smith had flown over this region in 1947 but hadn't seen much of the landscape below because of the rainstorm which drove them on to Fort Smith.

Other reports, information, and suggestions continued to flow in. A Royal Canadian Air Force pilot, who had flown in the north country for five years, wrote that he had sighted what he thought were whooping cranes. He gave the location as a group of tundra lakes south of Kugmallit Bay, east of Tununuk and west of Eskimo Lakes. This was up in the Mackenzie Delta region. The pilot went on to state that "unlike the common cranes, they live on the lakes in pairs and occasionally one bird by itself. These birds appeared to be of tremendous size," he added. The position of the sighting was 69 degrees 10 minutes North, 133 degrees 40 minutes West.

The pilot's report was one of the most encouraging received, for the birds he described certainly resembled whooping cranes. After passing the pilot's letter around, Allen and other biologists decided it was worth a search. Both the U.S. Fish and Wildlife Service and Canadian Wildlife Service were interested in making waterfowl surveys along the Arctic Ocean, and it was agreed that Allen and Smith would make these surveys in the summer of 1948. At the same time, they could scout the site suggested by the RCAF pilot, as well as any other likely areas in the far north.

Another interesting report came from a man who had considerable knowledge of and experience in the north country. He thought the most likely place to find the whooping cranes would be Lac la Martre (Marten Lake) and the surrounding area which lay between Great Slave Lake and Great Bear Lake. Allen also regarded this region as an important search area. There had been some old reports of whoopers sighted at Fort Rae and along the Anderson River farther up the Mackenzie River basin, so Allen added the region around Lac la Martre to the 1948 search list.

When the final plans had been drawn up, Allen continued his research and field work at Aransas. In April, twenty-eight whooping cranes left the refuge for the unknown breeding grounds. Shortly afterwards, on May 1st, Bob Allen drove from Texas to Saskatchewan, arriving in Regina on May 30th. Smith arrived the next day, and the two nest hunters prepared for their joint waterfowl survey and whooping crane nest search.

Allen and Smith left Regina in the Grumman Widgeon on June 3rd. Their first stop was at Prince Albert; then they headed for Alberta, flying over Watchush and Gordon lakes. There were forest fires in this part of Alberta and Allen and Smith were forced down at Fort McMurray. However, they were able to take off the next day and they flew up the Athabaska River to Lake Claire. At Lake Claire, the two biologists conducted duck surveys over 800 square miles of Lake Claire marshes and 500 square miles of Athabaska Delta. After completing the duck survey, Allen and Smith flew over Fort Chipewyan and on to Fort Smith in the Northwest Territories, just over the Alberta border. They had seen no whooping cranes in either the Lake Claire or Athabaska regions.

Flying out of Fort Smith, Allen and Smith traveled up the Mackenzie basin, staying close to the river, and went on to Fort Simpson. Finding no signs of whoopers, the two biologists flew on to Norman Wells. From this oil town they flew along the west side of the Mackenzie to Aklavik, which was to be their headquarters or base of operations while searching the far north country.

Aklavik—"the place of the brown bear," as the Eskimos called it—is at the extreme northwestern corner of the District of Mackenzie. Once a center of the fur trade, it later became an administrative center for the Canadian Government's communication, health, police, education, and related services for the District. In 1954, these services were transferred to Inuvik, which is east and across the Mackenzie River. The population of Aklavik is about 700 people, consisting largely of Loucheux Indians and Eskimos, plus a few white men.

The arrival of Allen and Smith in Aklavik was an occasion of some excitement, especially for the Indian and Eskimo children. Allen gave bird talks to them in the Anglican mission school, and the children were very interested in the whooping crane story and eager to hear about the hunt for the nests. They were also anxious to learn about the United States, and were astonished when Allen told them that the Texas coast—where the whoopers went in winter—had no snow or cold weather.

Allen and Smith made almost daily flights out of Aklavik on their search of the Arctic region. They coursed over a large portion of the Mackenzie Delta, including the Cape Dalhousie Peninsula which projects out into the Arctic Ocean northeast of Aklavik. They also inspected the tundra lake area suggested by the RCAF pilot, but found no trace of whooping cranes.

Next, they tried the section around the Anderson River where it flows into the Arctic Ocean at the village of Stanton east of Aklavik. This region teemed with ducks, geese, swans, loons, sandhill cranes, ptarmigan (Arctic grouse), caribou, and grizzly bears. But again, Allen and Smith saw no whoopers. Each time they returned from a search, they found the Indian and Eskimo children waiting for them at Aklavik. It was difficult to tell who was more disappointed at the failure to locate whooping cranes: the nest hunters or the children.

On July 4th, Allen sent the following report to John Baker at the National Audubon Society:

Aklavik, N.W.T., July 4, 1948

We have now covered all possible habitats in the Mackenzie Delta and east beyond the Anderson River. Not a sign of whooping cranes!

There's some fine country around Kugaluk River and eastward, the sort of thing we'd been looking for. There are great numbers of whistling swans and some little brown cranes (sandhills), but no whoopers.

On July 2, we went into Yukon country—up the Mackenzie and then east through Rat River Pass to Old Crow Flats. After running waterfowl transects across 1,000-foot-high flats, we landed in the swift waters of the Porcupine River and talked with the Mountie there and with Moses, the hereditary Loucheux chief. No whoopers in that country. Moses was a little uncertain, but he seemed to remember seeing such a bird near the Mackenzie River about fifty years ago. Douglas Oniak, an elderly Aklavik Eskimo, has similar memories. But there are none here today.

Our search here has covered nearly 16,000 square miles as follows:

Treeless Delta (Mackenzie)	1,600 sq. miles
Wooded Delta (Mackenzie)	3,600 sq. miles
Coastal Tundra (to Dalhousie)	900 sq. miles
Upland Tundra (east of the Mackenzie to the Anderson River)	5,300 sq. miles
Transition (south of Eskimo Lakes)	2,500 sq. miles
Transition (Old Crow Flats)	2,000 sq. miles

We've obtained an estimate of the waterfowl population of these areas and, in addition, have figures on the ptarmigan, little brown crane, loon, barren ground grizzly, caribou, and moose. We are certain that whooping cranes are not in the region covered. Between Great Slave Lake and Great Bear Lake there's one more possibility. It's difficult to judge from the maps, but it looks like about 3,000 square miles or more of waterfowl habitat, the only extensive area between Great Slave Lake and the Arctic Coast.

As soon as we pull our wheels and clear them of mud and silt, we'll take off for Point Barrow, Alaska, where we'll spend two days surveying the coastal tundra. Then, after some additional ground work here, we'll head for the final base at Coppermine. On our way out, we'll cover this last remaining possibility so far as whooping cranes are concerned.

We may finish our chores so as to be back in Regina as early as August 1st. We're both keeping well and getting a terrific kick out of the country and the natives. If I can get my hands on a Husky [Eskimo] drum, I'll do the Eskimo drum dance for you when I get back!

*   *   *

Allen and Smith made the trip up to Point Barrow and scouted the coastal tundra, obtaining a good waterfowl survey. They were not so fortunate as far as whooping cranes were concerned; there were none on the coastal tundra of Alaska. Upon their return to Aklavik, they were marooned for three days by a big storm. When the storm was over, Allen and Smith flew east over Bathurst Inlet at the southeastern end of Coronation Gulf in the central Canadian Arctic. They landed at Coppermine on the gulf. Here, they had two days of fine flying weather during which they scouted the tundra to Darnley Bay and searched the rugged muskox land to Bathurst Inlet. None of this region proved to be outstanding waterfowl habitat —and, of course, there were no whooping cranes.

Having exhausted all search possibilities in the Arctic coastal region, the two biologists took off on July 28th and headed south to the salt flats below Great Bear Lake. A storm blew up, forcing Smith to bring the Widgeon down on Hunter Bay in Great Bear Lake. Both men struggled for sixteen hours to keep the light plane from being smashed to pieces on the rocky shore; they literally held it down. When the storm lifted, they took off with a faulty generator. Smith just skirted the fringes of the salt flats, preferring to fly on to Yellowknife on Great Slave Lake. He was worried about the Widgeon's engine and thought it best to put down at Yellowknife, where it could be repaired.

They limped in to Yellowknife and Smith landed the plane with little difficulty. But when the mechanics checked it over, they found that the carburetor needed repair as well as the generator. The only place where this work could be done was Prince Albert in Saskatchewan. Smith and Allen decided to risk the flight and they managed to arrive safely in Prince Albert on August 4th. This was the end of the 1948 search for the whooping cranes. Between June 4th and August 4th, the two biologists had covered almost 42,000 square miles in their plane. But after all this flying and searching, they still hadn't seen a single trace of the twenty-eight cranes that had left Aransas in the spring.

*   *   *

In the fall of that year, two adult cranes and a young bird born during the summer circled over the south branch of the Platte River. They were the last family to leave the secret nesting grounds. Below them, the Platte flashed silver in the sun as it rippled past the sand bar where the whoopers had rested and fed in the spring.

Only four months old, the young whooper had performed very well on his first flight down from Canada. In the beginning, the youngster had trouble keeping up with the older birds, but the more he flew, the stronger he became. Now he no longer lagged behind, but he was glad of the chance to rest and feed.

Hidden in the bushes on the sand bar an old man and a young boy watched the cranes glide down from the sky.

"What did I tell you, boy?" whispered the old man as he carefully lifted the shotgun off his lap.

"Didn't I tell you I knew where to find them big cranes?"

Without taking his eyes off the three whoopers, the boy nodded. He felt excited and scared at the same time. This was his first big hunting trip and his uncle had promised him rare game for his initial venture. But now, as he gazed at the three beautiful cranes, he wasn't so sure that he wanted to shoot them.

The old man cradled the shotgun in his arms. He glanced quickly at some sedges and saw that the wind was blowing away from where he and the boy were hiding. They were downwind of the cranes, and only a sudden movement could alarm the birds. He leaned closer to the boy.

"Draw a bead on that little cinnamon-colored one," he whispered. "He's got the tastiest meat."

The boy gulped, licked his lips, and slowly raised the shotgun. The muzzle wavered to the right and left as he tucked the gunstock against his shoulder.

The old man slowly reached out and steadied the gun. "Steady, boy," he said in a low voice. "You'll only spray the river."

The young whooper paused only twenty yards from the boy, unaware of the danger. But the boy held his fire.

"Now, don't get buck fever, boy," said the old man

out of the side of his mouth. "That crane ain't
going to wait for you to make up your mind!"

The young crane waded in the shallow water near
the sand bar. Nearby, the two adult whoopers
searched for food.

"Now," said the old man between gritted teeth.
"Squeeze that trigger like I taught you."

The boy shook his head. "I don't think I should,
Uncle Bart." He lowered the shotgun quickly.

Up snapped the male crane's head. The sudden
motion of the gun had caught his eye. He hesitated
for just a second, then blared out his bugle call.
Ker-loo!

All three cranes started running, their wings held
aloft. The blast of the shotgun echoed across the
river and the young crane toppled over into the
water, its head floating limply in the gently coursing current of the Platte. The two adult cranes
leaped into the air and rapidly climbed high above
the sand bar, where they flew in agitated circles.

The old man ejected the shell and pointed to the
dead crane. "Least you can do, boy, is go get that
bird."

Walking slowly to the edge of the sand bar, the boy
picked up the dead whooper. He gazed up into the
sky where the two parents kept circling over the
sand bar. A plaintive *Ker-loo* drifted earthward.

He sighed and carried the dead whooper back to the old man.

"You almost scared them away," admonished the old man. "Lucky I had a bead on that crane." He looked furtively around and gestured to the boy. "Now, let's get out of here!"

All that day and the next, the two adult whoopers remained near the sand bar. They hunted through the sedges and along the riverbanks for their lost youngter—but they never found him. Only when the shouts of duck hunters broke the stillness of the river did the cranes rise into the sky, reluctantly pointing their heads to the south. And as they flew away, a melancholy *Ker-lee-oo!* floated back to the sand bar in the Platte.

The two whoopers were the last to arrive at Aransas that fall. When they came down to the salt flats, the other cranes, including three youngsters, were already feeding in the tepid waters of the sloughs and ponds.

EIGHT

The Hunt Slows Down—1949 to 1954

After four seasons of intensive search for the breeding grounds, the hunters still had no idea where the whooping cranes had hidden their nests. All of the most likely regions in Canada had been carefully scouted; all had failed to produce a single whooper.

Skeptics jeered at the failure of American and Canadian biologists to discover the nests. They could not or would not understand the difficulties of trying to find a handful of cranes in such a large wilderness as northwestern Canada. The majority of these scoffers had neither field experience in searching for elusive birds nor a familiarity with the remote territory that had to be carefully and painstakingly scrutinized.

Despite the failure to find the whooper nests, ornithologists and conservationists were not defeated or discouraged. True, they were baffled. But the reluctance of the whooping cranes to divulge the secret of their breeding grounds did not lessen the zeal or determination of the nest hunters. The trail would not be allowed to grow cold.

However, during the next three years there were no large-scale or extensive searches. Urgent duties elsewhere forced Allen and other biologists to devote less time to the search for the whooper nests. Actually, the only searches made were by U.S. Fish and Wildlife personnel and were in conjunction with regular waterfowl surveys. The indefatigable Bob Smith kept a sharp watch for whooping cranes as he conducted routine waterfowl counts in the Prairie Provinces and far north.

The task of compiling a life history of the whooping crane still occupied a considerable amount of Allen's time. From 1946 until 1952, he allotted a total of thirty-nine months to the Whooping Crane Project. Twenty-seven of those months were spent in the field in Texas, Louisiana, Oklahoma, Kansas, Nebraska, the Dakotas, the Prairie Provinces, District of Mackenzie, and the Arctic coast as far as Point Barrow, Alaska. Allen devoted the remaining twelve months to researching the literature on whooping cranes and writing his comprehensive report, *The Whooping Crane,* published in 1952 by the National Audubon Society.

Allen's report included all the known data on *Grus americana,* from prehistoric times to the present. The nature and habits of the big cranes, as well as their perilous situation, were brought into sharp focus. All in all, the report was a monumental work, and it established Allen as beyond doubt the first authority on *Grus americana*.

While the hunt for the whooper nests slowed down, public interest in the big cranes and their welfare gained momentum. Even so, the threat of extinction came closer during the period of 1950 to 1952. A total of twenty-four whoopers were lost in these three years. Seven cranes disappeared in 1950, eleven in 1951, and six in 1952. Nobody knew what happened to them; they simply failed to return to Aransas in the fall.

Although it was possible that these losses occurred on the nesting grounds, Allen and other ornithologists believed that most of them happened during migration. Fall was an especially dangerous time for the big cranes, what with hordes of hunters out stalking the rivers and marshes along the whooper flyway.

There also existed the possibility that farmers in Saskatchewan had shot some or all of the missing cranes. The fact that many Saskatchewan farmers were unsympathetic to the plight of the whooping crane was no secret to ornithologists and conservationists. These farmers were quite outspoken in their opinion that the hunt for the nests was ridiculous, a waste of both time and money. They advocated killing off the few remaining whoopers, thus saving the taxpayers' money, and some farmers openly threatened to shoot any whoopers that came their way. The danger area during the fall migration was the farming country south of the Beaver River in west-central Saskatchewan and on across the well-populated prairies to Rice Lake west of Saskatoon, Swift Current, Weyburn, and other small towns and villages down into North Dakota.

In an attempt to halt the loss of whoopers, a new publicity campaign was set into motion. The aim was to reach
all of the states along the migration route and the Prairie
Provinces, particularly Saskatchewan. As in the past campaigns, the major news media—press, radio, and television—were sent material on the big cranes. They all
agreed to do what they could to help promote the safety
of the whoopers. The state of Nebraska issued photographs of whooping cranes on the back covers of game
law booklets and hunting licenses. Under the photos was
the caption: DON'T SHOOT THIS BIRD!

The National Audubon Society sent educational leaflets
to Boy and Girl Scout organizations, 4-H Clubs, Future
Farmers of America, game departments, garden clubs,
nature groups, and school children in the migratory route
states. Numerous other organizations and many individuals offered their assistance and cooperation in the new
whooping crane publicity campaign.

Then came some great news.

In July, 1952, Bob Smith, flying over a remote region
north of Great Slave Lake, spotted two whooping cranes
just north of Deep Bay. He saw the first one on July 11th
and went back the next day for another look. The crane
was still in the area, about 200 yards from the site where
Smith had seen it the day before. The second crane was
discovered about thirty miles from the first one.

This was the best clue the nest hunters had found in all
the years of the search. But Smith's discovery didn't mean
that the breeding grounds had been located or that the
big hunt was over. It simply meant that whoopers were in
the Great Slave Lake region and that the field of search
had been narrowed.

In a letter to Allen, Smith reported that it was not practical to land a plane anywhere near where the cranes had been sighted. And working up to them on foot would be an exceedingly difficult task. He mentioned that both he and Allen had flown over this area twice: in 1947 and again in 1948. Had the whoopers been there then? There was no way of knowing.

Smith went on to say that he intended to make another observation of the whoopers in two weeks, on his way back from a waterfowl survey. But when Smith did fly back over the Deep Bay area, he found no trace of the whoopers. Once again, the birds had been swallowed up by the wilderness.

More reports on whoopers came in that year. One told of sighting whoopers over the Peace River in northern Alberta, and a geologist mentioned that he had seen what appeared to be a whooping crane three or four miles west of the Slave River, about halfway between Fort Smith and Fort Resolution. But neither of these cranes was sighted again.

Smith made another flight over the Deep Bay whooper site a year later, in June, 1953, but failed to see any cranes. He recommended to Allen that any plans for a ground search be postponed. In the same year, a Canadian helicopter pilot and an army officer based at Fort Rae reported a whooper—at least they thought it was a whooper—flying in an easterly direction, approximately twelve miles west of the outlet of Birch Lake, sixty-five miles southwest of Fort Rae. This sighting was near the region where Smith had spotted his two whoopers in 1952.

In the fall of 1953, the Chief of the Canadian Wildlife

Service, W. Winston Mair, announced that eight whooping cranes were reliably reported winging southbound along the Slave River. Things were starting to fall in place, and a definite pattern was taking shape. The nest hunters were now able to zero in on a specific target, an area that could turn out to be the secret hiding place of the whooping cranes. The exact location of the nests was still a mystery, but the big cranes had been observed in northwestern Canada and the trail was getting hot.

In April, 1954, twenty-four whoopers rose up from the Aransas salt flats, stretched their heads and necks northward and, with that unexplained instinct for navigation which birds possess, set a course for the Canadian northwest.

No definite plans had been made for Allen or Smith to conduct an organized search that summer. Allen was off on the trail of other vanishing birds, mainly the flamingos and reddish egrets. But Bob Smith and other Wildlife Service personnel were scheduled to make waterfowl surveys in Canada. If he or anyone else sighted whooping cranes, the National Audubon Society, U.S. Fish and Wildlife Service, and the Canadian Wildlife Service would hurry to take up the trail again.

Once more, as in the years past, the small group of whooping cranes passed over the U.S.–Canadian border into Saskatchewan and then quickly disappeared in the wilderness. Neither Smith nor any other Wildlife Service personnel saw them, and May and June slipped by with still no report on the cranes. It seemed as if the nest hunters were back where they started.

The skeptics came out in force and suggested that the

hunt be called off. But now there were more people and . organizations who spoke up for the hunt and the attempts to save the whoopers from oblivion. *The Christian Science Monitor* summed up the reason for the Whooping Crane Project with a fine editorial, "On Cranes and People":

There are twenty-six whooping cranes left in the world, says the National Audubon Society, two of them in captivity. And the Society appeals to sportsmen to save these great man-high birds from extinction by sparing them as they migrate from northern Canada to their winter refuge. Well, so what? The dodo bird and the passenger pigeon are already extinct. So, almost, are the trumpeter swan and the heath hen. And civilization seems to survive.

But does it, wholly? Can a society, whether through sheer wantonness or callous neglect permit the extinction of something beautiful or grand in nature without risking the extinction of something beautiful or grand in its own character? And the American society does have a conscience about such things.

That is why, over and above considerations of utility and necessity, the American people have endeavored to preserve the bison and the elk; why they have set aside national parks and wilderness areas from use either for private profit or even personal livelihood.

And that conscience is still a lively one. It may not understand everything about lumbering in a rain forest preserve or building dams in a national monument. It knows, however, that a civilization to survive must conserve as well as exploit, and that whatever conservation of the intangibles has been achieved has behind it unrelenting struggles. And so it is aroused and it protests when these intangible values in nature are threatened.

Some millions of Americans will hope, we are sure, that the whooping cranes are spared for their own sake. And we have an idea that most of them will at least sense, also, that each of these beautiful birds, as it flies southward, carries a Yellowstone or Quetico–Superior Wilderness [a Canadian park] between its great wings.

NINE

Success!

On June 30, 1954, William A. Fuller, a mammalogist
with the Canadian Wildlife Service, began another day at
his station in Fort Smith, Northwest Territories. Fuller's
basic duty was the study of mammals in the Fort Smith region and the southern part of the District of Mackenzie.
One of his projects was a study of the muskrats in the combined delta of the Peace and Athabaska rivers. After that
study was completed, Fuller turned his attention to the
bison in the Fort Smith area.

Fuller, of course, was aware of the hunt for the whooping crane nests. All zoologists in the Northwest Territories, even though primarily concerned with mammals,
had been alerted to watch out for the whooping cranes.
Fuller had flown on several flights with U.S. Fish and
Wildlife Service biologists on their waterfowl surveys and
whooper searches.

Bill Fuller had a strong background in biology. He grew up in Regina, obtained his bachelor and master degrees from the University of Saskatchewan at Saskatoon, joined the Canadian Wildlife Service, and was assigned to Fort Smith. On various occasions, Fuller had met with American and Canadian biologists who came to Fort Smith while on the hunt for the whooper nests.

On June 30, 1954, Fuller and other government personnel were informed that a fire was burning just inside the northwestern boundary of Wood Buffalo National Park, west of Fort Smith. This, in itself, was not unusual and the location of the fire was duly recorded.

* * *

Two whoopers and their three-week old chick were wading in the shallow water of the pothole. The mother whooper speared a pond snail with her lancelike bill, broke the snail into pieces and dropped them at her feet. Immediately, the chick darted at the food, uttering joyful squeaks. The snail fragments quickly disappeared.

Suddenly the male whooper lifted his head and pointed his beak to the northwest. His piercing yellow eyes carefully searched the landscape. He stood motionless for a moment, a northwest breeze rippling the feathers on his breast. Then he tensed as his nostrils were stimulated by the pungent tang of wood smoke. Again, the whooper's eyes swept the landscape with a thoroughness born of the need to survive in the wild. But he saw nothing out of place.

Thirty miles to the northwest, a mother black bear and her two cubs lumbered away from the flames that were shriveling the vegetation. A scared cub sat down on its haunches, and his whine lifted above the sound of the crackling flames. The mother bear whirled around, cuffed the cub on the side of the head, and forced him away from the oncoming fire.

A herd of wood buffalo, northern relatives of the plains bison, snorted and crashed their way out of the burning area. Leaping and plunging with an agility unusual for so ungainly an animal, a bull moose hurtled from the underbrush and waded far out to the relative safety of a pond. Waterfowl and land birds raced across the sky, their wings whirring loudly as they fled from the flaming area. The ducks landed far out in the pond, where they clustered together, squawking in terror and alarm.

Out of the burning brush, side by side, shot a timber wolf and a mule deer. The wolf's coat was badly singed and his eyes rolled wildly as he leaped into the pond. More animals bounded from the inferno: colored fox, lynx, mink, rabbit; all ran swiftly toward the wetlands east of the fire. Hunters and hunted, none of them concerned with anything but escape from the flames and hot embers flying through the air, shared the mutual terrors of the moment. And the aquatic animals—beaver and muskrat—made room in their pond for the wilderness refugees.

Meanwhile, to the southeast, the whooping cranes remained alert in their nesting grounds, ready to move farther out in the ponds and potholes. But the fire did not reach the nesting grounds; only the acrid smoke. The whoopers had selected their nesting grounds with a rare intelligence. Not only were the grounds inaccessible to most predators, but the patchwork of ponds, potholes, marshes, and lakes also served to contain any fire.

But suddenly a strange noise disturbed the stillness of the nesting grounds. It was a loud whirring, as if thousands of bird wings were churning the air over the ponds. The adult whoopers froze motionless, their heads cocked sideways, yellow eyes fixed on the huge dragonfly that flitted through the air from the southeast. Staring half-alarmed, half-fascinated, the whoopers watched the helicopter glide over their heads. Then it stopped and hovered for a few seconds before swinging around with flashing blades and coming back to the whooper family. Now it floated down toward them.

Ker-loo! The male whooper's call bounced around the pond.

Herding their chick before them, the two adult whoopers ran stiff-legged for the shelter of the tall sedges behind the nest. Above them hovered the helicopter, its two occupants leaning out and gesturing excitedly. Then the whoopers disappeared into the sedges. The helicopter lifted itself up over some spruce trees, whirled around, and buzzed

away to the northwest where fire number 24 was
still scorching the wilderness.

Around five o'clock on the afternoon of June 30th, the
pilot of the Forestry Service helicopter radioed to Bill
Fuller in Fort Smith and reported that he and his passenger, M. G. Wilson, Superintendent of Forestry, had
sighted three whooping cranes in Wood Buffalo Park.
Fuller was elated. He spoke to Mr. Wilson and learned
that the helicopter was due to make another trip to fire
number 24, and that he could accompany them.

Fuller was eager to fly over the reported whooper site.
As the resident biologist at Fort Smith, it was his duty to
confirm the report and then inform the Chief of the Wildlife Service.

The Forestry Service helicopter refueled at Fort Smith
and took off at 6:35 P.M., with Bill Fuller on board. Forty
minutes later, the pilot announced that they were over the
general area where the cranes had been seen. Below them
flowed the Sass River, and all around, as far as they could
see, was a region pitted with shallow lakes and ponds,
separated by zones of black spruce trees.

Fuller carefully scanned the ground below him. Then
he saw them: two adult whooping cranes! The pilot sent
the helicopter into a glide toward the cranes and they
took to the air, black-tipped wings beating frantically in
an effort to escape the mechanical dragonfly. Holding
the helicopter on course, the pilot followed the cranes,
allowing Fuller to take photographs. He obtained several
excellent ones before the whoopers disappeared into the
safety of the reeds.

Fuller wanted to examine the ground for whooper

tracks, and Don Landalls, the pilot, looked around for a safe spot on which to bring the helicopter down. However, the cranes had picked their site well; there was no suitable place to land. Even though he had to give up the idea of landing, Fuller was satisfied that the birds were indeed the long-sought whooping cranes. Landalls had brought the helicopter down close enough for all to see their black-tipped wings and red-patched heads. And the photographs Fuller had taken would provide additional proof.

The men had to cut short the inspection of the cranes and the site, since their primary destination was the fire up near the northwestern boundary of Wood Buffalo Park. Landalls swung the helicopter around and headed to the northwest. They reached the fire at 8:25 P.M., and as soon as the helicopter had settled on the ground, fire fighters quickly unloaded a fire pump and other sorely needed supplies. Landalls then lifted the lightened helicopter and headed back to Fort Smith. At approximately 8:40 P.M., the whirlybird crossed over an extensive patch of muskeg near the Nyarling River. Landalls spotted a lone whooping crane and dropped the helicopter to a lower altitude, giving Fuller a chance to photograph this whooper, an adult.

The trio arrived back in Fort Smith at 11:00 P.M., after fighting a headwind. Fuller immediately started to write his report. He was satisfied that positive identification of the whoopers had been made on the flights to and from the fire. The birds had been observed both on the ground and in flight. These cranes were in a region that lay between the Salt River and Fort Resolution, well within the boundaries of Wood Buffalo National Park in the Northwest Territories. From all indications, an extensive area of

Bison in Wood Buffalo Park, 1955
    by Robert Stewart, from the U.S. Fish and Wildlife Service

similar habitat was available to accommodate more whooping cranes.

This accidental discovery of the whoopers posed a question: Why hadn't cranes been observed in this region before? Probably because it was such deep and primitive wilderness, far off the usual paths of hunters, trappers, or tourists. In fact, summer travel on the ground was next to impossible. Furthermore, there was nothing to attract anyone to this remote area. It was a desolate place that was avoided by aircraft, even those equipped with floats or pontoons. None of the ponds or lakes was suitable for landing a plane.

But Smith and Allen had flown over the region several times; why hadn't they sighted any whoopers? Perhaps because the wilderness was so extensive, perhaps because there were so many places for the birds to hide. Whatever the explanation, it wasn't until fire number 24 frightened the wildlife and brought a low-flying helicopter over the area that the whooping cranes were observed at last. It was truly a stroke of luck.

Fuller dispatched his unemotional, factual report to the Chief of the Canadian Wildlife Service in Ottawa, detailing the original discovery by Landalls and Wilson and his own flight to confirm their sightings. The Canadian Wildlife Service personnel were jubilant over the finding of the whoopers in Wood Buffalo Park. A wire was sent at once to John Baker, President of the National Audubon Society, telling him about the discovery. Needless to say, everyone at the Audubon Society "whooped for joy"! Newspapers asked for more details, and inquiries came from as far away as Great Britain. The hunt for the whooper nests had attracted the attention of people in many foreign countries.

Soon afterward Baker received a letter from Winston Mair, Chief of the Canadian Wildlife Service, who wanted to know what course of action Baker thought should be taken that summer. Mair repeated Fuller's statement that the region was generally inaccessible, and also pointed out that it would not be possible to conduct an investigation at the nesting site without some disturbance to the whoopers. Judging from Fuller's report, the cranes were no longer on their nests, but still Mair felt it would not be wise to upset them while they were busy raising their young. Perhaps a full-scale ground exploration could be launched the following season.

Mair, like Baker and others involved with the Whooping Crane Project, was relieved to know that the nesting grounds were located in an established national park. If nothing else, that meant the whoopers were safe from civilization.

On July 12th, Baker telephoned Bob Allen, who was in Florida, and told him about the discovery of the nests. Allen followed up the call with a letter to Baker in which he wrote: "Our telephone conversation of this afternoon concerning the whooping crane reports from Wood Buffalo Park has been, for me, something like the clanging of a bell to an old fire horse!" It was ironic that Bob Allen, the world authority on whooping cranes and their most ardent champion, was not in on the discovery of the nesting grounds. But Bob was not a man to worry about who saw what first. He always kept his eyes on the main objective, and was not concerned about who would get the credit or glory.

Allen believed the whooper sightings in Wood Buffalo Park were the real thing. The location, date, and modest number of birds reported all fitted into a pattern. Allen also agreed with Baker and Mair that the season was too far along for a ground search. While the young whoopers would not be able to fly before late August, he believed the family units would range on foot over a large territory, thus making it extremely difficult to pin them down, let alone find them.

A few weeks later the Chief of the Canadian Wildlife Service wrote again to John Baker. He stated that the

latest observations of the whooper sites in Wood Buffalo
Park showed that at least two pairs, a young bird, and a
lone adult were in the region. Canadian Wildlife Service
personnel would make limited helicopter flights over the
nesting sites and adjacent areas to determine whether
there were any more whoopers in the vicinity.

The Chief also advised Baker that the Canadian Wildlife Service would alert persons living along the migration
route from Wood Buffalo Park southward to watch for the
fall flight. He concluded that it would be reasonably possible to assure protection for the cranes in Wood Buffalo
Park. In accordance with this, the Canadian Government
was restricting aircraft activity over the region.

Mair thought that even though it might prove difficult
to locate the whoopers during the breeding season, it was
important that an effort be made. The information that
could be obtained by observing the cranes during that
time would be of great value in their future management.
He suggested that any ground exploration be made by experienced personnel, preferably from the National Audubon Society, U.S. Fish and Wildlife Service, and the
Canadian Wildlife Service. The use of experienced biologists would reduce the disturbance of the cranes. And the
less publicity or fanfare, the better it would be for all
concerned—especially the birds themselves.

The three agencies holding stewardship over the
whooping cranes decided on a ground search in the summer of 1955. The first phase of the plan would be to send
Bill Fuller on aerial surveys over the nesting sites as soon
as the ice broke up. This might be around May 15th, possibly earlier. Fuller's mission would be to spot the

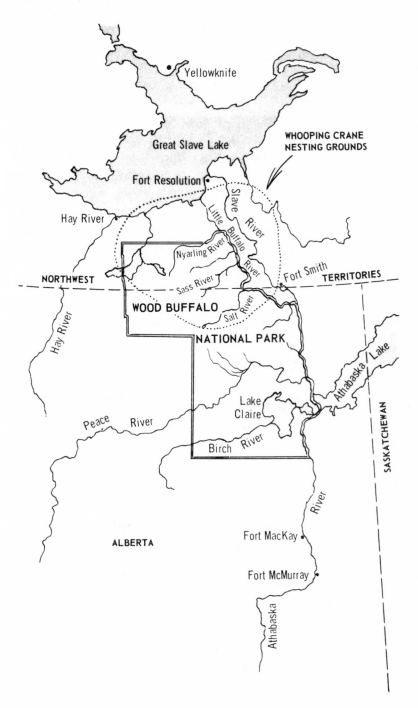

Wood Buffalo National Park and Surrounding Region

presence and location of pairs of whoopers before they
settled down to the job of building nests. Once this was
accomplished, Fuller would relay the location of the
whoopers and a ground team would move into the region.
The National Audubon Society and U.S. Fish and Wildlife Service were each invited to send at least one repre-
sentative for the team. After ten years of fruitless search,
it was hoped that man would again see a whooper nest
close up.

*   *   *

Unconcerned as yet over the discovery of their secret nesting grounds, the whooping cranes again
headed south in the fall of 1954.

Nearly 2,000 miles away, Aransas biologists
awaited the arrival of the big cranes. As always,
they asked each other: "How many will come back
this year?"

The biologists checked in the whoopers one by
one, like fighter planes or bombers returning from
a mission. When winter was close at hand and the
last whooper had arrived from the north, a dismal
fact made itself known. Not one youngster had
survived the flight from the nesting grounds. It was
the first time that the Aransas biologists had to
chalk up a zero in the young-of-the-year column.

And out of a total of twenty-four adult whoopers
that flew north in the spring, only twenty-one came
back to the Aransas sloughs.

TEN

On to the Nesting Grounds—1955

Wood Buffalo National Park is a wilderness area of 17,300 square miles which bisects the boundary between the Province of Alberta and the District of Mackenzie, Northwest Territories. Set aside as a national park by the Canadian Government in 1922, it is the home of the largest wild bison herd in the world. Originally, only wood buffalo, or wood bison, roamed the region. (Wood bison are larger and darker than their southern relatives, the plains bison.) Between 1925 and 1929, almost 7,000 plains buffalo were herded north into Wood Buffalo Park. Today, the present herd of bison, consisting of an admixture of wood and plains buffalo, is estimated to number between 14,000 and 16,000 animals.

The park's greatest length—a route from the southern border directly north to a point on the confluence of the

Nyarling and Little Buffalo rivers—is approximately 176 miles. Its average width is more than 100 miles. Nearly two thirds of this tremendous park is in Alberta; the balance is in the District of Mackenzie. Wood Buffalo Park is so large that all of Canada's seventeen other national parks could be placed within its boundaries.

The park is managed by the Northern Administration and Lands Branch of the Department of Northern Affairs and Natural Resources. Direct control of the park is in the hands of a Superintendent, aided by a staff of wardens and patrolmen who are responsible for wildlife management and protection and the enforcement of park regulations. Park wardens and patrolmen also cooperate with forestry personnel in detecting and fighting fires, as well as the inspection of any timbering operations going on within the park.

Most of Wood Buffalo Park's terrain is flat or gently rolling land, but it also includes the Birch Mountains in the southwest, and the Caribou range which lies to the west. These mountains rise to a height of 1,500 feet above the surrounding plains. They are actually plateaus, a result of erosion during the Cretaceous age, and are the source of numerous swift-flowing streams.

In the central part of the park is the Alberta Plateau, a region distinguished by many shallow lakes, ponds, and sluggish streams. There are also a number of low hills, actually moraines, scattered throughout the central portion. These moraines, composed of chunks of mountain rocks and other geological debris, were deposited by the glaciers. An underlayer of limestone stretches beneath a large section of the Alberta Plateau, and there are limestone escarpments along the eastern boundary.

In between the limestone escarpment and the Slave River flood plains is a narrow prairie called the Salt Plains. The soil on this prairie has a high salt content, due to springs which come from the base of the escarpment. Men and animals have long made use of the salt mounds in this area. Alexander Mackenzie obtained salt from them while on his famous exploration trip to the Arctic Ocean, and today countless animals visit the Salt Plains to satisfy their craving for the mineral.

Sinkholes perforate the eastern sector of the Alberta Plateau within the park's boundaries. The sinkholes were formed by the action of subsurface waters dissolving the limestone base. Many of the sinkholes are dried up, but a few contain water. In some areas they have spread out and joined together, and their combined waters form small lakes, such as Pine Lake. This particular sinkhole lake is three and a half miles long and has a depth of sixty-five feet. Its waters are crystal clear, and the surrounding beaches are sandy.

Wood Buffalo Park is a natural paradise for all kinds of wildlife. In addition to the bison herd, other large mammals include moose, woodland caribou, mule deer, and black bears. Occasionally, the rarer Barren Ground caribou wanders down from the north. Elk were reintroduced into the park in 1949. The natural enemy of the large grazing animals, the timber wolf, also roams the region.

Many smaller mammals are found throughout the park. Streams and rivers are well stocked with beavers. Muskrats busy themselves in the marshy delta regions. Colored fox, mink, ermine, and lynx are other common fur-bearing animals living within the park's boundaries. All told, forty-six species of mammals have been observed there.

Wood Buffalo Park abounds in birdlife, too, with more than 200 species and subspecies appearing on its bird list. Many of them are summer residents familiar to bird watchers in eastern Canada and the United States. One of the largest accumulations of waterfowl is found on the Peace–Athabaska Delta in the fall, and ruffed, sharp-tailed, and spruce grouse are plentiful. Out on the lakes in the interior portion of the park, the solitary loon's tremulous call can be heard echoing back from the surrounding wilderness. Eastern and western gulls hover and quarrel over the better fishing areas, mainly at the foot of the Slave River rapids near Fort Smith. North America's most northern colony of pelicans is also located within the park. And now the whooping crane can be added to the bird list of Wood Buffalo Park.

During the winter and early spring of 1955, the three partners in the Whooping Crane Project worked on plans for the ground exploration of the nesting sites. Since preliminary observations from the air would be necessary, the use of a helicopter was a vital consideration. There were helicopters available on a rental basis, but the Chief of the Canadian Wildlife Service announced that no funds could be allocated for one that summer; some other type of aircraft would have to be used. A float-equipped plane could be rented, but its practicability in the wilderness of Wood Buffalo Park was doubtful, since there was no suitable place to land it.

This news created a serious complication. Aerial observations were vital to the ground exploration plan, and a plane would also be needed to carry men and supplies to a base camp. Later, when the ground search team was pushing over treacherous terrain, the men would have a rough time finding the target without guidance from the air. Furthermore, canoe routes into the whooping crane area were not very navigable; in fact, it was questionable if they could be used at all. Ernest Thompson Seton, the noted naturalist and author, had once made an unsuccessful attempt to penetrate this wild region by canoe.

In March, 1955, Bill Fuller wrote Allen that the possibility of chartering a helicopter was still very remote. But he advised Allen that aerial photographs of the whooper nesting sites would be taken and made available to the ground search team. Fuller himself planned to fly over the places where the whoopers had been seen the previous year, and he would try to plot them on aerial maps. If this could be done, then the ground team might find its way to the nesting sites with less time and effort.

By mid-April, the last of the twenty-one whooping cranes left Aransas and were on their way to Canada. Fred Bard sighted five of them flying over Saskatchewan. He managed to take clear photographs of the cranes and reported his observations to Fuller in Fort Smith. Upon receiving Bard's report, Fuller knew that the whoopers would arrive in Wood Buffalo Park any day now. Sandhill cranes and snow geese were already on the Salt Plains west of Fort Smith.

Fuller had at his disposal a conventional plane, the Beaver, equipped with skis. But the season for ski-equipped planes was drawing to a close. Word came that the runway at Fort Smith—normally snow-covered from fall to spring—was deteriorating fast and would not be usable for more than a few days. This meant that the Beaver would have to be flown to Yellowknife on Great Slave Lake for the removal of the skis and replacement with wheels. Fuller knew very well that wheels were not the best landing gear for the muskeg areas where the whooper nests were located, but once they were on, the plane could at least take off and land on the Fort Smith runway. Later, the plane could be refitted with floats for possible landings on lakes.

After the Beaver's skis had been exchanged for wheels, Fuller decided to make a flight over the whooping crane territory on April 29th. But low ceilings and snow showers moved into Fort Smith and vicinity, delaying the flight. Fortunately the weather cleared somewhat the next day, at least enough for the plane to take off. The Beaver, with two passengers, the pilot and Fuller, skimmed over the Fort Smith runway, rose up quickly, and headed for the Sass River.

They soon ran into snow showers, but managed to proceed on down the Little Buffalo River to the place where it joins the Sass. The pilot guided the plane along the Sass and into the whooper territory. Luck was riding with Fuller, for he soon sighted two whoopers in a lake about a half mile from the Sass. These birds were within one mile of the site where Fuller, Landalls, and Wilson had observed cranes in 1954.

The plane circled the lake above the whoopers at an altitude of 800 feet, but neither of the two cranes seemed disturbed by it. They kept on with their search for food

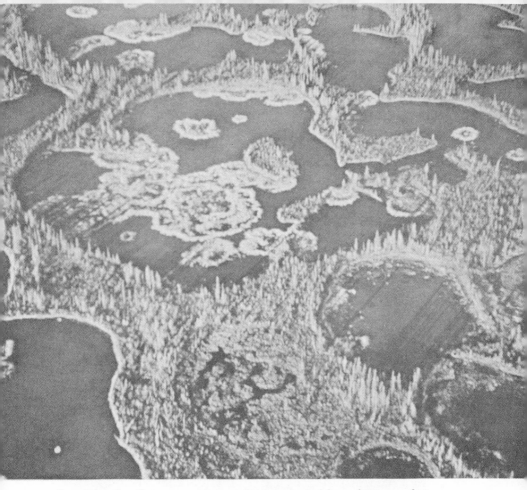

One of the whooping crane nesting ponds, photographed from about 1,000 feet
by Robert Porter Allen, from National Audubon Society

while Fuller took photographs of them, and the surrounding region. Later on, he planned to line the photographs up with the aerial maps.

Suddenly the weather worsened and snow showers began to obscure the pilot's vision. Fuller did not waste any time trying to locate more whoopers, but instructed the pilot to take the plane back to Fort Smith. After his return, Fuller sent a detailed report to the Chief of the Canadian Wildlife Service, together with his suggestions for the ground search. He was optimistic about the chances of a ground party working its way into the whooper sites. The Sass River—Sass is the Chipewyan word for bear—was navigable, at least in the spring and early summer. One foreseeable snag presented itself: there were plenty of beaver in the Sass and this meant beaver dams, which would make canoeing difficult.

Fuller thought that a base camp could be set up on the Sass and be supplied by air drop. The ground party should be provided with a radio which would enable the searchers to maintain communication with the Wood Buffalo Park network. He considered the Sass as the logical place from which to operate, since the whooper nests were fairly close to the river.

There were three routes to the Sass River: (1) by road to Buffalo River falls, then down the Little Buffalo River and up the Sass—this route could be used only if and when a fallen bridge over Salt River was replaced; (2) down the Slave River and up the Little Buffalo River from its mouth at Great Slave Lake—this route could not be used until the ice cleared in Great Slave Lake; and (3) down the Slave River to Grand Detour, then over a six-mile portage to the Little Buffalo River.

In Fuller's opinion, the last route, number 3, was the most practical way of reaching the whooper nesting grounds. Equipment and supplies could be carried by skiff to the portage, and extra men could be hired for a day to carry the gear and supplies over it. He recommended that the ground party get under way as soon as possible. An early start would bring the search team into the waterways when the rivers were at a high water level. Also, there was the important fact that the whooping cranes nested early. For these reasons, Fuller urged that the ground party be ready to leave Fort Smith no later than May 15th.

Meanwhile, Bob Allen was on his way to Great Inaqua Island in the southern Bahamas to conduct a study of flamingos for the National Audubon Society. He landed at Matthew Town and shortly afterward was handed a radiogram from John Baker, instructing him to leave for Fort Smith right away. He dropped the flamingo investigations, caught a mailboat, and traveled to the States via Nassau.

Arriving in Florida on May 8th, Allen found a detailed letter from John Baker waiting for him. From the letter he learned that Fuller was unable to go on the ground search, since he was required to represent the Canadian Wildlife Service at the Alaska Science Conference. However, Fuller's assistant, Ray Stewart, would go in his place, and the U.S. Fish and Wildlife Service would be represented by Bob Stewart. The two Stewarts and Allen were to rendezvous at Fort Smith by the middle of May.

While Allen was making preparations to leave Florida for Fort Smith, Fuller and Ray Stewart scouted the whooper site in a Northwest Mounted Police aircraft. A lone whooper was sighted on the upper Sass. The next day, Fuller and Stewart made another flight over the area, this time in a chartered plane. They saw a crane crouching over a large brown patch on a swampy island. The plane circled the site several times, allowing Stewart and Fuller a clear view of the crane, which continued to hover over the patch. Since the whooper did not leave it, Fuller concluded that the bird was guarding a nest.

On May 18th, Fuller and Stewart again visited the whooper sites. This time they flew with Ed Wellein and Wes Newcomb of the U.S. Fish and Wildlife Service in a Grumman Goose. Four pairs of whoopers were sighted. Two cranes stood beside a nest close to the Sass River, and another two cranes were seen at a nest north of the Klewi River. Northwest of the other sites, they saw a lone whooper take to the air over a nest containing a single egg. Two more whoopers were spotted farther east on the Klewi. It was a rewarding trip for the biologists and ample proof that the whooping cranes were residents in Wood Buffalo Park.

During these flights Ray Stewart carefully scanned the Sass River, from its juncture with the Little Buffalo to the whooper sites. He was checking for special landmarks which the ground search party could use as guideposts. Near the Sass, about a mile upstream from the whooper nests, he noted an escarpment of limestone. This escarpment could be used as a reference, or bench mark, by the team working its way overland to the nesting grounds, and a base camp set up near the escarpment would prove a useful point from which to scout the whooper nests.

The more Stewart flew over the Sass, the more he realized how troublesome it could be. It was a winding river —more like an oversized creek—with deep and fast water. As far as Stewart could see, the ground party would be forced to portage around the beaver dams.

This aerial survey was the last one of the season, for Fuller had concluded that there was nothing more to be gained by flying over the whooper sites. From now on, it would be up to the ground party. Allen and Bob Stewart arrived in Fort Smith and listened attentively while Fuller briefed them on the aerial surveys and whooper sightings. He omitted nothing; every detail, from the water level of the Sass to the location of the nests, was held up for examination and discussion.

Allen set about the task of making arrangements for the ground search. There were innumerable items to consider. Equipment had to be secured, food ordered, pack carriers hired; timetables had to be set up, communications checked, and other chores put out of the way before the ground party moved out of Fort Smith. Nothing could be overlooked. The ground exploration promised to be a rugged mission, one that might possibly last eight to ten weeks. There would be many days spent in the brush and marshes, and a forgotten item could bring hours of discomfort or frustration.

On May 23rd, Allen, the two Stewarts, and ten Chipewyan Indians set out down the Slave River in a large skiff with a high bow and outboard motor. A canoe rode the water behind the skiff. Forty-four miles downstream from Fort Smith, the Indian packers readied themselves for the portage over the Grand Detour—an expanse of prairie between the Slave and Little Buffalo rivers.

Grand Portage, the overland route from the Slave to the Little Buffalo, consisted of a beautiful, remote prairie, with spruce timber yielding to a wide sea of waving grass stretching many miles north and south. The Indian packers trudged through the tall grass with the equipment and supplies. Allen and the two Stewarts paused to watch a flock of sandhill cranes fly past, their musical call of *hur-roo-oo-roo-roo* sounding loud and clear over the great

The Little Buffalo River, near Grand Detour Portage, 1955
by Robert Stewart, from the U.S. Fish and Wildlife Service

prairie. Off to the south, a hawk swung around in the sky,
quartering the prairie in search of prey.

The party made good progress over the Grand Portage
and arrived at the Little Buffalo. Their part of the trip at
an end, the Chipewyans set down the equipment, supplies, and food. When they learned that the white men
intended to go down the Sass, they shook their heads. The
Sass was not an easy river to navigate. But the Indians
didn't voice their skepticism and offered no comments. It
wasn't their affair; if the white men wanted to tussle with
the Sass and mosquitoes—well, it was up to them. The

Chipewyans had been hired only to carry the packs to the Sass, and this they had done. They waved good-by to the ground party and headed back to the Slave River.

Allen and his teammates found the Sass swift and tortuous. That by itself would not have been insurmountable, but the river was also choked with log jams and blockaded by strong beaver dams. And since the time Fuller and Ray Stewart had made the aerial surveys, the water level of the Sass had dropped several feet, exposing the massive log jams and making them more formidable. It didn't require an expert to see that the light canoe was useless under these conditions. The party was stymied. Another sour note set in when it was discovered that the radio was faulty. It received broadcasts from the Wood Buffalo Park network, but could not transmit.

Allen and Ray and Bob Stewart looked at each other in consternation. This was a fine predicament! A log-jammed river, faulty radio, and useless canoe before they even entered the whooper territory. Allen fiddled with the radio. Fort Smith kept calling them, asking for their position and requesting a reply. The frustrated searchers could only listen. Unable to get a response, Fort Smith broadcast an alert to all ranger stations to be on the lookout for the ground party. The broadcaster then told Allen that a search plane would go into the area and try to locate them. Allen was instructed to send up smoke signals.

This was too much for the ground party and they let off some steam by way of verbal expletives. They didn't want to be rescued! Maybe after they found the whooping cranes, a rescue party could come in after them. But not now. There was no way to communicate with Fort Smith and hold off a rescue party. Allen decided the best thing to do was to reach a ranger station and explain the situation.

There was only one way for them to go: down the Little Buffalo to Great Slave Lake. The water in the Little Buffalo was high enough to float the canoe. After caching the equipment and supplies, the thwarted nest hunters started down the Little Buffalo. They made the 85-mile trip, through fast water and rapids, in eleven and a half hours. But more trouble awaited them at Great Slave Lake; that huge body of water was still frozen. Some Chipewyan Indians, also stranded because of the ice, told them the only way to travel was to walk. It was sixteen miles to Fort Resolution by way of the lake shore. Allen and the two Stewarts started to hike, but were soon stopped by snowdrifts. One of the Chipewyans then volunteered to make the trip to Fort Resolution and deliver a message. After the Indian left, the weary and disgusted ground party pitched camp on the shore of Great Slave Lake. Two days later they were picked up by a plane en route from Hay River to Fort Smith.

It was discouraging and embarrassing for the party to limp back to Fort Smith after such a short trip. But the nest hunters had no intention of giving up the search. Allen located a helicopter in Hay River, a town on the southwest shore of Great Slave Lake. The owner was flying oil geologists on surveys. He agreed to rent the whirlybird to Allen for a trip into the whooper territory, and the float-equipped Beaver was also available for a few days.

The teammates worked out another plan. The Beaver

could ferry the ground party and supplies to a lake selected on the aerial map, twelve miles south of the Sass
River campsite. From the lake, the helicopter would then
ferry men and matériel to the campsite. Since the nearest
whooper nest was three miles down the Sass from the
proposed campsite, Allen also decided to take the light
canoe as a means of transportation into the whooper
site.

According to plan, the Beaver deposited the party
and supplies on the lake near the Sass, and on June 5th,
the rented helicopter floated down out of the sky. The
pilot was not too cooperative; he wanted to get the job
over with in a hurry, and impatiently went over the flight
plan with Allen.

Allen's idea was to have the helicopter fly due north
to a point twelve miles from the lake. When the limestone
escarpment, charted by Fuller, was sighted, the pilot was
to bring the helicopter down as close to the riverbank as
possible. There the biologists would set up the base
camp.

Since Ray Stewart had been over the area by plane, he
was elected to go on the first flight. Altogether, four flights
were made between the lake and the campsite, each
round trip requiring about an hour. After the last trip,
the helicopter pilot took off in a hurry, eager to get out of
that wilderness with its swamps and mosquitoes.

Camp was set up on the riverbank about a mile and a
half downstream from the limestone escarpment. Once
the routine chores were out of the way, Allen and his
partners looked around them. They were in a wild, remote region never before explored by white or red man.

A thick stand of white spruce formed the background, while the log-glutted Sass twisted through the brush and spruce trees.

The next few days were spent in exploring the region and fighting off the mosquitoes. All the exploration was on foot; any thought of riding in the canoe had been jettisoned. The logs in the Sass, many of them with sharp limbs projecting above or just under the water, would soon have punched holes in the light canoe and swamped the nest hunters.

Accompanied by their halos of mosquitoes, the searchers pushed their way through the brush in the direction of the whooper nests. After struggling to the estimated distance, they still found no whoopers. Repeated side trips also failed to turn up any cranes. Slapping at mosquitoes, the baffled nest hunters sat down to figure things out, and gradually the truth emerged. They were in the wrong area. Somehow or other, the helicopter had put them down near the wrong escarpment. In short, they must be lost.

And this was true. The pilot had put them down at the base of another escarpment, not the one charted on Fuller's aerial map. The compass variation in that particular region of Canada was between 32 and 33 degrees easterly. It was apparent that the pilot, either through ignorance or carelessness, had not taken this variation into consideration. He had flown northeast instead of true north, as Allen had requested, and this error in navigation meant that the ground party had pitched camp within a mile and a half of the Sass River's mouth!

Lost, marooned, and plagued by satanic mosquitoes,

the three men could do nothing but sit it out. They had no way of getting a message to Fort Smith, since the radio still could not transmit. The best they could hope for was that a rescue party would come after them.

All three men were experienced biologists and naturalists and kept themselves busy while awaiting rescue. They performed camp chores and fought the mosquitoes. Bob Stewart marked out an area and made a nesting bird census. They sat around the campfire at night and talked about whoopers and life. And when the night was well along, they crawled into their sleeping bags and left their troubles until tomorrow.

Six days later, Bob Smith, on his way to the Arctic coast for a waterfowl survey, flew over the area and spotted the campfire. In the plane with him was Ward Stevens, Superintendent of Game for the Northwest Territories. Stevens dropped a message for the lost nest hunters. It told them that they were less than two miles from the Little Buffalo River! They were also informed that the helicopter company would be advised of their predicament. In the meantime, Allen and his party were to stay at the campsite.

They waited. Eleven days after the helicopter pilot had set them down near the wrong escarpment, a radio message came through on the Wood Buffalo Park network, telling them that the helicopter was no longer available. They would have to get out of the area in whatever way they could. There was no possibility of a ground rescue party reaching them and the use of another helicopter was very remote.

Again, the nest hunters were forced to retreat before reaching the whooping cranes. While the air distance

Camp on the Little Buffalo River, 1955
   by Robert Stewart, from the U.S. Fish and Wildlife Service

from their erroneous campsite to the Little Buffalo River
was only a mile and a half, the trip took thirteen hours of
backbreaking work. Chased by clouds of mosquitoes,
hampered by log jams and beaver dams in the Sass, the
three biologists literally clawed their way to the Little
Buffalo River. After caching the supplies at the same spot
they had reached more than a month before when they
first left Fort Smith, they recrossed the Grand Portage and
staggered into Fort Smith on June 21st.

This second retreat was more humiliating and discouraging than the first. And now, with no helicopter to ferry

them to the correct campsite, it seemed that there was nothing left to do but abandon the ground search for that year. It was a difficult decision, especially when the nest hunters had been so close to the breeding grounds. But without a helicopter it was impossible to reach the whoopers. Bob Stewart took the next commercial plane to Edmonton, and from there he continued on down to the States. Allen and Ray Stewart remained at Fort Smith to wind up the ill-fated ground search.

*   *   *

The big cranes had selected their nesting grounds with an eye to safety and privacy. Their nests and young were well protected by natural barriers. Muskegs, potholes, thick growths of reeds and sedges, beaver dams, log snarls, and formidable outposts of mosquitoes and black flies held off any hunters. No guns blasted the stillness of the nesting grounds because no man could enter their domain on foot or by boat. It was a natural fortress.

Those predatory animals which lurked on the perimeter of the breeding grounds were constantly kept under the wary eyes of the adult cranes. Few animals were rash enough to run the gauntlet of the birds' lancelike beaks or a thrashing by their powerful wings.

Undisturbed for many years, the whoopers felt secure in their secret nesting grounds. As far as they were concerned, their fortress would always be impregnable. They did not know that man could now fly like the birds.

*   *   *

Allen and Ray Stewart had just about completed arrangements to leave Fort Smith. Neither man wanted to quit, especially since the objective was known. And both were reluctant to admit that they had been bested by Nature. They had each faced hardships before, grappled with difficult field conditions, and emerged victorious. But neither man had ever run up against a combined force of adversities like that which had rebuffed their attempts to reach the cranes' nesting grounds. Like it or not, Nature had simply thrown too many barriers in front of them.

Still smarting from their defeat, Allen and Stewart packed their gear. They were tired, and studded with welts from countless mosquito bites. But despite their exhaustion the two biologists were still hoping for some timely reprieve. And it came. Allen was handed a message which stated that a helicopter belonging to the General Air Transport Company was available. Both men roared their approval and shouted the news to any and all who came their way. They were to have another crack at the nesting grounds!

The happy biologists lost no time in planning another assault on the whooper sites. They feverishly checked over the equipment, made up a new food list, and scanned Fuller's aerial maps with a magnifying glass. There could be no mistaken escarpment this time. The over-all plan for this trip was similar to the previous one. The helicopter pilot would pick them up on the same lake as before and ferry them and the equipment to the Sass. Allen and Stewart vowed that they would set down alongside the right limestone escarpment this time or die in the attempt.

The Canadian Wildlife Service placed its motorboat, the *Buffalo,* at their disposal. Sailing down the Slave River in the *Buffalo* on the first leg of their new attempt, Allen and Stewart rested for the ordeal ahead. Fastened to the bow of the motorboat was a wooden barge. It was to be used as an emergency landing strip for the helicopter.

They did not have long to wait at the designated helicopter rendezvous. General Air Transport's helicopter, piloted by an experienced flier named Holmgren, arrived on schedule. Holmgren was a likable man from the American South who had served in the Korean War. Unlike the first helicopter pilot assigned to the search, he was adventurous, confident, and ready for any kind of action. Having flown whirlybirds off the battleship *Missouri* during the war, he wasn't fazed by the prospect of dropping the helicopter down on the tangled shore of the Sass River. Holmgren's confidence rubbed off on Allen and Stewart, and the two biologists climbed into the mechanical dragonfly, ready for anything.

Guided by Stewart, Holmgren whirled the helicopter toward the Little Buffalo River, then turned up the Sass. Allen and Stewart stared down at the treacherous Sass with mixed feelings. Twice the river had thwarted them in their attempts to reach the whooper nests. But this time it would be another story. Holmgren slowed the helicopter while the biologists made a careful aerial reconnaissance, constantly referring to Fuller's maps. Landmarks were examined over and over, for neither man wanted another costly navigational error. Finally, after pinpointing the right escarpment, Allen signaled Holmgren to take the helicopter down.

The ace pilot nodded, sent the helicopter dropping toward the twisting Sass, and set it down almost exactly on the spot indicated by Allen. The gear was unloaded quickly, and Holmgren lifted the helicopter for another run back to the lake. While he was gone, Allen and Stewart sorted the equipment. Holmgren was back in a short time, fluttering the helicopter down near the pile of supplies. When the last of the provisions had been safely stacked on the campsite, Holmgren waved good-by to the biologists. He was under instructions to return the helicopter as soon as possible. Elevating the whirlybird above the heads of the biologists with a blast of stirred air, Holmgren waved once more, swung the plane around, and flitted off to his home base.

Allen and Stewart gazed around at their surroundings and breathed a loud sigh of relief. They were at the right escarpment. After thirty-one days of toil, sweat, mosquitoes, black flies, log jams, and other pesky frustrations, they were now within shouting distance of the whooper nests at last.

It was late afternoon and the day was sultry and hot. A heavy moist air pressed down, forcing the two men to breathe in gasps. Both of them were tired from the heat, labor, and strain, but there still was work to be done. They pitched the tent, cached the food, and stacked the equipment where it would be ready for instant use. Then, when the camp was in satisfactory order, they curled up and slipped into a well-earned sleep.

They awoke early the next morning refreshed in body and spirit. After cooking and eating a hearty breakfast, the two biologists set out to find the whooper nests. The

Robert Stewart (left) and Robert Porter Allen (right), 1955
U.S. Fish and Wildlife Service photo

nesting sites, according to Fuller's maps, lay to the west of
the campsite across a large brûlée, or burned-over area.
The brûlée turned out to be a tricky obstacle; it was soft
and mushy, and the men had to pick their footing with
care. Walking became more and more difficult as they
headed due west across it. Although the morning was still
young, a hot sun beat down on them and they were soon
soaked through with perspiration. To add to their discomfort, the black flies and mosquitoes joined forces with the
sun to impede their progress.

Slapping at insects and wiping the perspiration from
their eyes, Allen and Stewart finally reached the end of

White spruce forest near the Sass River, 1955
by Robert Stewart, from the U.S. Fish and Wildlife Service

the brûlée. Ahead lay a forest jungle of stunted birch, willow, tamarack, and black spruce trees. Fortunately, judging by Fuller's map, this rugged terrain was the last barrier between the hunters and the whooper nests. The two biologists pushed into the thick growth, staying on a westerly course. Visibility became very limited. At times, they could see no farther than fifty feet around them. They made frequent stops to get their bearings, consulting the map for orientation. Then a mass of brush and dead trees suddenly loomed up before them. For the time being, their path was blocked.

Exhausted, soaking wet with perspiration, and itching from countless insect bites, the two men sat down on a log. First they would get some much needed rest. Then they would tackle the job of hacking their way through the brush blockade. Fatigued as they were, they felt elated. Somewhere, not far from where they rested, were the whooping crane nests.

* * *

Only one crane braved the hot sun beating down on the pond. The others had retreated into the shade of the reeds and sedges. The lone crane, a male, remained on guard. He waded into the tepid water near the reeds that sheltered his mate and chick. Now and then, he jabbed his bill into the water and captured a snail. But soon the glaring sun proved too much for him and he walked, stiff-legged, toward the hideout of his mate and chick.

A slight sound caused him to stop. His yellow eyes scanned the brush to the right of him. He stood motionless, head cocked slightly to one side. Then he heard the sound again. It was a whisper, a sound the whooper had heard down in Aransas. It was a human voice.

Up snapped the whooper's head. He swung quickly around and faced the direction from which the sound came. His whole body quivered with tension, and his eyes dilated as he saw a man slowly emerge from the brush. Man and bird stared at each other across the narrow inlet of the pond. Neither made a move. Then another man joined

the first and they crouched on the edge of the brush, silently watching the great crane.

A faint breeze stirred and wafted the man-spoor toward the crane. He strode quickly away from the men, hoping to draw them off his hidden mate and chick. But when he looked back over his shoulder, he saw that both men remained by the brush.

Ker-loo! The alarm shattered the stillness of the pond and echoed and re-echoed around the wilderness. Up rose the whooper with strong wing-beats, climbing high above the nesting grounds. He swung around in a short circle, sending repeated alarms down to the other cranes.

Out from the reeds and up into the air rushed the other adult birds, clucking warnings to their chicks. While the big cranes flew around to divert the enemy, the chicks withdrew deeper into the reeds and sedges.

But the men who watched the cranes were not the enemy. They were friends. And they had come a long way to proclaim their friendship.

*   *   *

Allen and Stewart grinned at each other in triumph. They could barely restrain themselves from shouting a victory cheer. Ignoring the bites and stings of the black flies and mosquitoes, both men peered through binoculars at the circling cranes. The nesting grounds of the whoopers were a secret no more. After more than ten years of searching over the Canadian wilderness, man and cranes were united on the breeding grounds.

Approaching closer to the reeds and sedges, the biologists saw a whooper nest. This was the final victory. Allen and Stewart were the first men to see a wild whooping crane nest at close range in more than thirty years. And the biologists silently agreed that the sight was worth all the toil and frustrations.

The next ten days were spent in exploring the whooping crane nesting sites. The biologists hiked to the lake where Bill Fuller had sighted the cranes the year before, when flying with Landalls and Wilson to the forest fire. Allen and Stewart decided to name it "Discovery Lake."

While inspecting the nesting region, the two men collected specimens of plants, minerals, and pond organisms. They compiled a list of birds and mammals seen in the area. Extensive notes were kept on the general character of the nesting sites and the natural protective barriers. Both men busied themselves from morning to evening during the ten days. Then it was time to return to Fort Smith and report their findings to the scientists and interested public who were eagerly awaiting news of the ground search. Only now Allen and Stewart returned in triumph.

The discovery and exploration of the whooper breeding grounds was exciting news to thousands of persons who had followed the search over the ten years. Americans and Canadians were now assured that the whoopers nested in a safe place.

The search had been a long and arduous one, but some of the long-pending questions had been answered. The nesting sites were located in a wild, unknown, and lost region. There was adequate food and water for the big cranes and their young. Predators presented no major problem; only man could reach the whoopers and cause them harm. Since the cranes nested in Wood Buffalo Park, a refuge under the protection of the Canadian Government, perhaps even man need not be feared.

The great nature hunt ended victoriously. Admittedly, it was not a world-shaking event, like the launching of a man into outer space. Yet it was a milestone to the people who still saw beauty in the natural history of a great continent. And it might be said that a piece of North America was rediscovered along with the whooping crane nests.

How The Whoopers Fare Today

Much has happened to the whooping cranes since Bob Allen and Ray Stewart set foot on the nesting grounds in Wood Buffalo Park. First of all, the world's only wild whooping cranes have made a valiant comeback from the dangerously low population of only fourteen adults and four juveniles seen in the late 1930s. At that time, the rare whooping cranes, standing over five feet in height and with a wingspread of seven to eight feet, faced the same fate of some other birds: total extinction.

Gone are the great auk, Carolina parakeet, heath hen, Eskimo curlew, Labrador duck and the passenger pigeon. These birds were sent into oblivion, never to be seen again except as dusty specimens in museums. Destruction of habitat, overhunting and trapping caused the disappearance of these North American species.

The great auk, America's only flightless bird, was so thoroughly hunted and killed that by the first quarter of the nineteenth century it was a rare bird. Although an excellent surface and underwater swimmer, the great auk was helpless on land. It was an easy feat to step up to an auk and club it to death. And that is what happened to hundreds of these birds.

The great auk, after being ruthlessly hunted for more than two hundred years, was sent into extinction. It was the first North American bird to be handed this fate. On June 3, 1844, Jon Brandsson and Sigourour Isleffson killed the last two great auks on Eldey Island, off the southwest coast of Iceland. The eggs of the two birds were also destroyed.

Nobody knew how many passenger pigeons existed in North America at the beginning of the twentieth century. It was estimated that millions of passenger pigeons darkened the skies all over America. They were the poor man's game birds, plentiful and easy to trap or shoot. And they were trapped and shot in great numbers. The pigeons were preyed on by Native Americans, white hunters and trappers, as well as various wild-bird and mammal predators.

The last large gathering of passenger pigeons occurred on a site near Petasky, Michigan. However, in 1878, this huge roosting place was cleared of all its pigeons. After that, the passenger pigeon joined the ranks of rare birds. In 1898, the last wild passenger pigeon disappeared from the earth. Only one live specimen remained, in the Cincinnati Zoo, but died on

September 1, 1914. That was the end of this once numerous and popular bird.

The heath hen, a widely distributed North American prairie chicken, was a popular game bird in the northeastern states. This wild chicken lived in the grasslands, pine barrens and blueberry regions in New England south to Virginia. It was a fowl of the pot; tasty, easy to hunt and sought by many. Into the pot went so many heath hens that the last one was recorded on the eastern mainland in 1869. It followed the great auk and passenger pigeon into extinction.

Overkill and habitat destruction pushed the Eskimo curlew, Labrador duck and Carolina parakeet over the brink and into extinction. Three other North American birds teetered on the edge of extinction: the whooping cranes, trumpeter swans and California condors. All three have been the focus of cooperative recovery programs.

By the end of the nineteenth century, no more than a thousand trumpeter swans remained in North America. Swanskins, which included the feathers, were in great demand in the late nineteenth and early twentieth centuries by manufacturers of ladies' clothes. Swan hunters from the United States and Canada invaded the wetlands, trapping and shooting the trumpeter swans. Arthur Cleveland Bent, one of America's noted ornithologists, forecast the extinction of the trumpeter swans.

An actual census taken in 1935 revealed an alarming fact: only 73 trumpeter swans were to be found in North America. Wildlife biologists knew that the last of the trumpeter swans congregated in a wild, remote region known as Centennial Valley. This wilderness lay between two mountain ranges in southwestern Montana. Beyond these mountains, in Yellowstone National Park, a few trumpeters hid from civilization.

Fortunately, the rare trumpeter swans were not without friends. One of them was the late Jay N. Darling, Chief of the United States Bureau of Biological Survey. Darling, a former *New York Herald Tribune* cartoonist, was concerned about the declining trumper population. He and other conservationists realized that if the trumpeter swans were to be saved, they needed a wildlife refuge.

Some of the land in Centennial Valley was publicly owned, some in private hands. Two fine lakes were situated in the valley: Upper and Lower Red Rocks Lakes. Both provided ideal habitats for the dwindling trumpeters. Consequently, The Red Rocks Migratory Waterfowl Refuge was established in 1935, with an initial purchase of nearly 23,000 acres. Here, in this splendid locale, aided by hunting prohibitions and sound management methods, the trumpeters staved off extinction.

The whooping cranes, along with the California condors, trumpeter swans, and snowy egrets were also endangered. In the southern marshes, lagoons and bayous, egrets were hunted to the point of near extinction. In the late nineteenth and early twentieth centuries, women's hat fashions demanded large feathers and milliners paid good prices for the feathers of egrets, herons and spoonbills. But it was the snowy egret that suffered a sharp drop in populations. These birds attained their best plumage during the breeding season, the time when plume hunters converged on the rookeries and slaughtered the birds.

The plume hunters wanted only feathers from mature birds and did not, as a rule, kill young birds. However, hundreds of nestlings starved to death when their parents were killed. Eggs did not hatch and rotted in the bulky nests. In a short time, the rookeries in the southern swamps no longer resounded with the harsh calls of hundreds of egrets.

One woman decided to do something about the slaughter of the egrets. She was Minnie Maddern Fiske, the celebrated American actress. Mrs. Fiske enlisted the aid of friends and launched a crusade to save the egrets. She was especially irate when she learned that the aigrettes — the name given to the plumes of egrets — were the nuptial plumes of the female egret. The efforts of Mrs. Fiske, the New York Zoological Society and Audubon Clubs focused public attention on the plight of the egrets.

Largely through the efforts of Mrs. Fiske and conservationists, public sentiment for the egrets mounted. Most American women rallied to the cause and shunned hats with feathers. But a hard core of wealthy women persisted in wearing hats with aigrettes as a symbol of their wealth and social position. Eventually the fad for feathered hats collapsed and long feathers became unfashionable. One year after Mrs. Fiske's crusade, the southern swamps once again echoed with the calls of hundreds of egrets.

The California condor is an endangered species. Encroachment by civilization on their habitat, pesticides and poisoned predator bait threatened the rare condors. However, conservation and protection measures are in force to save this ancient vulture species. A special team of United States Wildlife Service biologists, known as the Condor Recovery Team, set about capturing the birds as the first step in preventing their extinction.

By April of 1987, all but one of the few existing condors had been captured and placed in refuges. The holdout condor, known as AC-9, escaped capture for fifty-one days, warily avoiding the traps set for it. However, the last of the free-flying condors was taken as it fed in the Bitter Creek National Wildlife Refuge (once the Hudson ranch estate). AC-9 was taken to the San Diego Wild Animal Park.

The capture of AC-9 brought the total of condors in captivity to twenty-seven. Fourteen condors were housed in the San Diego refuge and thirteen in the Los Angeles Zoo. There were thirteen males and fourteen females. Biologists hoped the captured vultures would breed and thus help to save the species. The condor captive breeding program was a success. The flock of condors grew from the 27 endangered birds in 1987 to 90 condors today.

Radio telemetry has been employed to track released condors in southern California over the past four years. The condor-recovery plan calls for the establishment of three or more populations with a minimum of 150 birds per colony. Each of the prospective populations of condors must be self-sustaining, with 10 to 15 breeding pairs.

Populations of condors have been planned for Arizona and Utah by the U.S. Fish and Wildlife

Service. However, public hearings held in northern Arizona and southern Utah in 1996 brought forth opponents of the plan. A main objection to the establishment of condor populations in these two states was that the condors would "impact existing land uses." Some objectors declared the condors to be "nonessential" and "experimental birds." A similar objection was raised in California over the release of condors in that state. The condors released in California face threats from existing land use. And condor conservationists insist that the big birds be classified as an endangered species and not "nonessential" or "experimental birds."

As for the whooping cranes, their slide toward extinction has been halted by the dedication and work of American and Canadian biologists and conservationists. Perhaps of all endangered birds, the whooping cranes have been the center of public attention ever since the Aransas National Wildlife Refuge was established in 1937. Magazine articles, newspaper items, scientific papers and television films have all kept the valiant struggle of the cranes to escape extinction before the public.

The whooping cranes have been subjected to a variety of studies, in the field and in research centers. Migration routes, roosting sites, food sources and consumption during migration, habitat use, environmental and man-caused disturbances have all been added to the whooping crane dossier. The data obtained from these studies have made it possible to plan and implement various population-recovery programs.

The wild whooping cranes now exist in two major

migratory flocks. It was decided that a natural or man-
made catastrophe could wipe out the original
Aransas/Wood Buffalo flock. This flock still winters at
the Aransas/Matagorda Island National Wildlife
Refuge Complex on the Texas gulf coast. The second
migratory flock is located in the Grays Lake National
Wildlife Refuge near Wayan, Idaho. These migrate to
the Bosque del Apache National Wildlife Refuge in
south-central New Mexico.

In 1975, the United States Fish and Wildlife Service
and the Canadian Wildlife Service co-sponsored a project that created the second migratory whooping crane
flock. Dr. Rod Drewien placed whooping crane eggs
from the Wood Buffalo Park flock in the nests of sandhill cranes in the Grays Lake National Wildlife Refuge.
The aim of this project or experiment was to have the
sandhill cranes hatch and rear whooping crane chicks.

If this experiment worked out, the sandhill cranes
were expected to guide the young whoopers to the
Bosque del Apache National Wildlife Refuge in New
Mexico. The cranes would travel approximately 850
miles, while the Aransas/Wood Buffalo Park flock had
to travel what could be a dangerous 2500-mile journey
in their annual migrations.

There were great expectations for this "cross foster-
ing" experiment. The sandhill cranes hatched and
reared whooper chicks. And the young cranes migrated along with their foster parents. However, when the
whoopers reached breeding age biologists were disappointed. Although breeding behavior among whooping cranes was observed, nothing came of it. No nesting, eggs or chicks resulted. "At least one cross between

whoopers and sandhills is known," according to Mike Fisher, Manager of the Grays Lake Refuge. But this whooper-sandhill hybrid did not return to the Grays Lake Refuge. The practice of placing whooper eggs in sandhill nests was discontinued in 1989.

Fisher reported that in 1996 there were four whoopers in the Grays Lake or Rocky Mountain flock. Only one returned to Grays Lake. This small flock faces predation by golden eagles, coyotes, and other mammalian predators. Grays Lake adult cranes are subjected to collisions with power lines and illegal hunters. And there is always the possibility of an outbreak of avian tuberculosis.

Not much was known about the food habits of the Aransas/Wood Buffalo Park whooping cranes at the time of the search for their breeding grounds. To be sure, the diet of the cranes wintering at the Aransas refuge had been studied. But little was done in the way of learning what and where the cranes fed during their long migration trips.

Migrating cranes, according to Michael J. Armbruster in a U.S. Fish and Wildlife Report (Biological Report 90 (4). "Characterization of Habitat Used by Whooping Cranes During Migration,") make use of both animal and plant foods. When on dry land or in prairie country, the cranes feed on corn, barley, wheat and sorghum. In the wetland their diet consists of frogs, tadpoles, crayfish, small-fish species, salamanders and insects.

Armbruster points out that adequate and suitable cover is an important factor in the safety of the cranes during migration. The cranes usually prefer wetlands

for their roosting sites. Such sites include open fresh
water, shrub and wooded swamps, bogs, ponds, lakes
and fens. Whooping cranes and sandhill cranes rarely
roost in water deep enough to reach their "tibio-tar-
sus/tarsometatarsus joints," according to Armbruster.
Dr. Lawrence H. Walkinshaw, author of *The Sandhill
Cranes*, found this depth to be about 28.1 cm for
female cranes and 28.6 cm for males.

Another important safety factor for the migrating
whooping cranes is security in the roosting sites. Clear
horizontal visibility, according to Armbruster, is crucial
for the safety of the cranes. The cranes must have a
clear view of any approaching or impending danger.
Whooping cranes, shy and retreating birds, are affected by various human activities. Among them are paved
and gravel public roads, private roads, railroads, commercial developments, recreational areas and parks,
bridges and powerlines. Powerlines are a serious haz-
ard for the migrating cranes.

Habitat loss, pollution, mining operations, oil
drilling and the filling in of wetlands are problems for
the cranes. When the intercoastal canal was created, "it
cut through the marshy feeding areas of the whooping
crane," according to Beverly Fletcher, ranger at the
Aransas/Matagorda Island National Wildlife Refuge
Complex. Ms. Fletcher pointed out that the most hazardous traffic on the canal are the chemical barges. If
chemicals spilled from these barges, the cranes would
be immediately affected. Furthermore, an oil spill in
the Gulf of Mexico would present a danger to the
cranes.

Raccoons, foxes and other predators are always a

Cranes kept together to form a cohort or band of birds before shipping to Kissimmee refuge.

by Jonathan Male, Patuxent Research Center

Whooping crane being introduced to new habitat at the Kissimmee refuge in Florida.

by Jonathan Male, Patuxent Research Center

threat to the whooping cranes, particularly the chicks. Dry spells or droughts diminish wetlands, thus making it easier for raccoons and other mammals to reach whooper nests and chicks. In 1982, some hunters killed seven raccoons that killed sandhill cranes and a captive whooping crane named "Tex."

Tex made avian history when she hatched a chick from an artificially inseminated egg. Dr. George Archibald, director of the International Crane Foundation in Baraboo, Wisconsin, achieved notoriety when he spent six weeks mate-dancing with Tex to bring her up to a breeding condition. When Dr. Archibald was notified of the death of Tex, he stated "I was attached to that bird." Tex's only offspring, "Gee Whiz," started life as a healthy chick one foot tall.

Disease is always a problem in any flock of birds, wild or captive. The whooping cranes are not exempted from this risk. In 1984, seven whooping cranes in the Patuxent Wildlife Research Center in Maryland died from eastern equine encephalitis. It was the first time the organism for this disease had been isolated in whooping cranes. How did the cranes contract the disease? They were nowhere near any horses. Diligent research revealed that the disease had been transmitted to the cranes by the *Culeseta melanura* mosquito. Oddly enough, this mosquito did not transmit the equine encephalitis organism to horses! Or to human beings. Research-center biologists were further puzzled when they learned that the mosquito bred in water that accumulated in hollows or depressions in tree roots in swampy bottomlands. No such conditions existed at the Patuxent Wildlife Research Center.

Three years later, fourteen cranes died from an unknown disease at the Patuxent Research Center. Among them were three whooping cranes. More than 100 cranes of different species became ill. Thirteen cranes were placed in isolation pens. There was no evidence that the cranes had been infected with the equine-encephalitis organism. The sick cranes improved when treated with vitamins, fluids and antibiotics.

By 1988, the whooping crane population was rebounding, despite losses from disease, accidents and predation. That year, the Aransas/Wood Buffalo Park flock produced twenty-two chicks which were banded by Canadian wildlife biologists. That same year, 134 whoopers spent the winter at the Aransas refuge. However, the Grays Lake flock did not fare so well. Fifteen whoopers were lost as a result of predation and a prolonged drought. Nevertheless, the increase in whooper populations was encouraging. Wildlife biologists thought the number of cranes might exceed 200 birds with good luck. If this proved to be true, that number of cranes would be the highest count in the twentieth century.

The Aransas/Wood Buffalo Park flock had its best year in 1995, according to Brian Johns, Wildlife Biologist with the Canadian Wildlife Service, Prairie and Northern Region. In a letter to the author, he stated that 1995 "was a year of several records for the Canadian flock. There were forty-nine nesting pairs, at least forty-five chicks hatched in June, and twenty-eight of them survived the migration and are wintering on or near the Aransas National Wildlife Refuge." And in the winter of 1996, Beverly Fletcher, Aransas Refuge ranger, reported 128 adult whooping cranes and twenty-eight chicks wintering at or near the refuge. This was the highest number of whoopers since a count began in the late 1930s.

Brian Johns reported that at the present time, "there are no known environmental hazards adversely affecting the cranes. The nesting grounds in Wood Buffalo Park are protected under the Canadian Parks Act and are declared a 'special Preservation Area' within the park." What this means is that access to the crane habitat is prohibited except for researchers involved in the whooping crane rehabilitation program. This is an important safety measure for the still-endangered cranes.

At this writing, eighteen whooping cranes are in the Devonian Conservation Research Center, a branch of the Calgary Zoo, Botanical Garden and Prehistoric Park located in Calgary, Alberta. In 1992, a whooping crane breeding program was initiated at the Calgary Zoo. Four juvenile whoopers were flown to Calgary from the Patuxent Wildlife Research Center. Additional whooping cranes for this breeding program were to come from surplus eggs from the Wood Buffalo Park flock which would probably not hatch there; transplanting cranes from the Grays Lake flock; and birds from the breeding programs conducted at the Patuxent Wildlife Research Center and the International Crane Foundation at Baraboo, Wisconsin.

The Calgary Zoo whooping crane breeding program is not intended solely as a means of producing cranes for display. It is also an international conservation project, a contribution to the preservation of a rare and endangered species. A long-range aim is to reintroduce whooping cranes to their historic breeding grounds. To date, no chicks have been hatched in the Calgary Zoo. However, the youngest pair of cranes on record did lay some eggs, an encouraging sign.

A whooping Crane Recovery Plan worked out by Canadian and United States wildlife biologists included establishing a flock in Florida. Accordingly, fourteen juvenile whoopers raised at the Patuxent research center and the International Crane Foundation were transferred to Florida's Kissimmee Prairie. The pairing problem with the whoopers raised by the sandhill cranes at Grays Lake was not expected to occur in the Kissimmee flock. These cranes had been raised by human beings wearing whooping crane costumes and were imprinted on the bogus cranes.

Since they were already in a warm, wintering habitat, the Kissimmee whoopers were not expected to migrate. For one thing, they had no adults to teach them a migration route. The failure to migrate, however, was a safety factor. The cranes would not have to run a gauntlet of power lines, illegal hunting, and other hazards. But the Kissimmee cranes had some problems. In the first year of their transfer to the Kissimmee Prairie, nine of the cranes were killed by bobcats. More cranes were transferred to the Kissimmee Prairie and by 1995, fifteen whoopers had survived in their new habitat. Plans called for adding twenty chicks each year, thus forming the basis of a nonmigratory whooping crane flock.

Once the three wild whooping crane flocks are stabilized and self-sustaining for the next decade, it may be possible to reclassify the cranes from an endangered species to the status of a threatened species. But it is to be expected that the wild whooping cranes will continue to be subjected to fluctuating numbers. Loss of cranes to predation, disease, habitat loss and collisions with power lines are dangers the cranes still face. More studies and work have to be done in the ongoing efforts to preserve the big cranes. However, and for the time being, they have been held back from extinction.

Captive whoopers cavort in snow-laden enclosure.
—*Patuxent Environmental Science Photo*